Stories for
YOUNG TEXANS
Call of the Southwest

by

J. A. RICKARD

Professor of History and Government
Texas College of Arts and Industries
Kingsville, Texas

and

CLYDE INEZ MARTIN

Associate Professor of Elementary Education
University of Texas
Austin, Texas

Illustrations by
WM. R. SOWELL
FIORE MASTRI
and
BILL NEALE

W. S. BENSON & COMPANY

Publishers   Austin, Texas

STORIES FOR YOUNG TEXANS

Books in the Series:

CALL OF THE SOUTHWEST

FROM OLD LANDS TO NEW

Contents

Contents

Call Up Adventure and Let Us Ride

Call up adventure and let us ride,
Careless and free by the trappers' side;
Call up the wild processions again,
Of painted tribes and Mountain Men;
Savage and restless and r'arin to go,
In hot pursuit of the buffalo.
O'er high sierra or burning plain,
Let us ride the Old Frontier again.

— *James Daugherty*

To Boys and Girls:

The authors of this book have written and selected stories especially for you. These recordings of the past will help you to understand what your country and state are today; they will give you a desire for fun, adventure, study, and success because years ago children of earlier times had the courage and the great determination to solve their own problems.

The landing of Columbus at San Salvador caused the European countries to explore America. They sailed first along the coast of the New World, and afterward they went inland and on into the Southwest. Here the mild climate, rich soil, and varied minerals—wonderfully developed through training and freedom of effort—have made the area a happy place in which to live.

The history of the Southwest is interesting and colorful. Young Texans will enjoy the gripping stories of this period in which its heroes do and dare as they make explorations and discoveries in a new country inhabited by Indians, wild mustangs, longhorns, and buffaloes.

THE AUTHORS

Call of the Southwest

"Moses Austin! If I am not mistaken, that is who you are."

Call of the Southwest

The Successful Beginning

He must have been well past fifty years of age, if a tired face and stooped shoulders were indications of years. His uncut hair showed plainly below his coonskin cap, as he limped slowly across the main plaza at San Antonio de Bexar. The raw December wind made him shiver as he faced it, but he hunched his shoulders and kept on going. On his face was a look of utter despair, but his eyes became curious as a huge man strode toward him. The man was smiling and holding out his hand.

"Moses Austin! If I am not mistaken, that is who you are."

"That's right, and you — you're — ?"

"Baron de Bastrop. We met in Louisiana some years ago. Remember?"

"Yes, I certainly do recall that meeting; and I'm happy to see you again. That was after the United States had bought the Louisiana Territory. You were engaged in some colonizing work, I believe."

"Yes. And now I am a Spanish citizen and live here. But my friend, you look discouraged! Tell me about yourself."

Moses Austin told him about his family in Missouri, how he had worked hard to make a living there operating lead mines, and how he had lost his money when the Bank of St. Louis failed. Then he had decided to come to Texas, secure a grant of land, and start a colony. He had made the trip of eight hundred miles on horseback, through unknown country.

"But now all is well," replied Bastrop heartily. "You will like Texas. And I'm sure the Spanish governor here will help you get a land grant."

Moses Austin shook his head sadly. "No, he refused to help me. In fact, he ordered me to leave town before night. I was on my way to get my horse; the one tied yonder to the hitching post."

"Why that — that's unheard of! More settlers and a colony are what Texas needs. But why did he order you to leave?"

"He said he had orders from Military Commander General Arredondo (Ä-rä-dōń-dō) not to permit any foreigners, and especially any people from the United States, to enter Texas. He said I probably wanted to take Texas away from Spain as Nolan, Long, and some others had tried to do. At least that's what I *think* he said; I couldn't understand him very well."

"Couldn't you make him understand that

you were different from them? Or maybe you couldn't speak Spanish with him."

"I tried to talk to him in French, but he wouldn't listen. He did most of the talking. He wouldn't look at my papers showing me to be a Spanish citizen. I became one when I was living in Missouri, which was in the Louisiana Territory while Spain owned it. Instead of looking at my papers, he ordered me to leave."

The Baron looked at Austin closely. "But you can't leave today. You are almost sick and are in no condition to travel. I know what we'll do. Come with me and we shall talk over the matter and decide upon a plan."

Wondering, Austin turned his horse over to his servant, Richmond, and followed Bastrop. He had trouble in keeping up with his long-legged host, but after a short walk, they stopped in front of a rambling adobe house with an inner patio. Bastrop led his guest to a bedroom and bowed him into it.

"Now I am going to turn doctor, if I may," Bastrop said kindly, "and my first prescription is that you go to bed."

Austin obeyed the order, then fell asleep. When he awoke, his new friend told him that he had been to see Governor Martínez (Mär-tĕ́-nāz).

"I have his permission for you to stay in the city another day, and I also have an ap-

11

pointment to talk with him about you and have you meet him. Now tell me more about your colony."

Austin told him and showed him his papers and plans. Bastrop was even more hopeful than he had been earlier.

"Why, a colony like that would be a success from the start," he said. "Texas has land in huge amounts. All it needs is people."

"I can get them, never fear. Right now my son is in New Orleans, and he will start them this way as soon as I give the word."

Patio of the Spanish Governors' Palace in San Antonio

"Then stop worrying. We will see the governor tomorrow, and maybe he will change his mind. I have quite a bit of influence around here."

Moses Austin was ready to believe that statement the next day when he went with Bastrop to see the governor. The Spanish official met them with a smile, and he was especially friendly to Bastrop. This time he listened carefully when Bastrop explained the colony project of his friend.

"Why, of course, of course," he agreed. "A colony would be a good idea. Give me your petition, and I will send it to the Spanish officials in Mexico."

Austin gave him the petition, which he had already prepared, and the governor promised to have an early meeting of the ayuntamiento (a-yoōń-tä-mē-ān'-tō — town council) to go over it. Then, he said, it would be sent to Mexico City.

A few days later Austin had the satisfaction of knowing that the petition or request was on its way to Mexico. If it should be approved there, it would permit him to settle a colony of Americans at any place in Texas which he might select.

He decided not to wait for news as to whether the petition had been granted. It was four days after Christmas, and he was eager to start home. Both Bastrop and the governor were certain the request would be granted, but it would take two months or longer to hear from Mexico City. Austin prepared to leave.

"I want you to be my agent here," he told Bastrop. "You were the one who saved me from failure."

"Your Spanish citizenship helped," Bastrop replied. "But I'll be glad to represent you. As soon as I learn the decision of the Spanish officials, I will notify you."

After shaking hands warmly with his friend and agent, Moses Austin started back toward his Missouri home. He was happy, for he felt that his mission had been accomplished. Austin and his servant, Richmond, began the long return journey on horseback, as they had come to San Antonio.

Natchitoches, Louisiana, was their first stop. The trip was a hard one. Much of the time it was raining, the weather so cold that at times their clothes froze to their bodies. While they were camped on the Trinity River, a panther jumped from a tree and started toward them.

"Look out!" cried the Negro in terror, as he fled. Austin held his ground and shouted loudly at the animal. Luckily, the panther was startled and ran away.

According to later stories by Richmond their

food supply ran low, and for the last eight days they had only roots and acorns to eat. Some of the streams were so full of water from rains that the travelers had to swim them. When they reached the home of Hugh McGuffin, about twenty miles from Natchitoches, Austin was a sick man.

He finally recovered enough to be able to make his way toward his Missouri home by steamboat, rather than horseback. His nephew, Elias Bates, was now with him, the Negro having been left behind.

Though at last reunited with his family, he never recovered from his illness. He always believed that the Spanish officials would grant him the right to establish a colony, but he did not live to accomplish that work. On June 10, 1821, he died at the home of his daughter, Emily Austin Bryan. The great work of his life had only been planned; others had to carry out his plans.

— J. A. Rickard

Things to Do

1. Read aloud the part of the story that tells how Moses Austin looked as he limped across the plaza in San Antonio.

2. Discuss the reasons for the following facts with your classmates. Re-reading parts of the story may help you:

   a. Why was Moses Austin's trip to San Antonio important in the history of Texas?

   b. Why was he discouraged when he met Bastrop?

   c. Why did the Spanish governor refuse to listen to Austin?

   d. How was Bastrop able to get the governor to see Austin?

   e. Why did Austin leave for his home in Missouri without waiting for an answer from Mexico?

   f. Why did Moses Austin's plans have to be carried out by someone else?

3. Who finished the task that Moses Austin had started?

Their only dependence for subsistence was upon wild game

Austin's First Trip to Mexico

Mary Austin Holley was a relative of Stephen F. Austin. In 1836 she wrote about some of the hardships that Austin endured in order to start a colony in Texas. His father, Moses Austin, had been given a grant of land for the colony, but died before he was able to establish it. Here is Mrs. Holley's story:

At his death, Mr. Moses Austin left a request that his son, Stephen F. Austin, should undertake the enterprise which he had thus started, of forming a settlement in Texas. Stephen F. Austin . . . immediately entered upon the

17

prosecution of the enterprise with vigor . . . .

In March, 1822, Gen. Austin went to Bexar to make his report to the Governor, by whom he was informed, for the first time, that it would be necessary for him to proceed immediately to the City of Mexico. [This was] in order to get from the new Mexican Congress a confirmation of the original [Spanish] grant to his father, Moses Austin, and receive special instructions as to the distribution of land, the issuing of titles, etc.

* * * Hasty arrangements were made with Mr. Josiah H. Bell to take charge of the infant settlement, and General Austin immediately departed for the City of Mexico, a journey of twelve hundred miles. * * *

Finding no opportunity of obtaining an escort, and the business of the colony requiring his presence in the city, he resolved, at all hazards, to proceed on his journey. They traveled the first day unharmed. On the morning of the second day, feeling somewhat ill, he undertook to prepare some coffee. There were no accommodations on the road, and it was necessary to carry provisions on a pack horse, and cook by the way-side. His companions warned him, that if there were Indians near, they would be attracted by the smoke. . . . They were upon an open plain, and they could see many miles around.

No living creature at the moment, but themselves, was in view.

. . . The general retired to a little ravine to enjoy his coffee. It was boiled; and in the act of putting the refreshing beverage to his parched lips, he heard a sound like the trampling of many horses. Raising his head, with the coffee yet untasted, he beheld in the distance, fifty mounted Comanches, with their spears glittering in the morning sun, dashing towards him at full speed. As the column advanced, it divided, according to their usual practice, into two semi-circles, and in an instant he was surrounded. Quicker than thought he sprang to his loaded rifle, but as his hand grasped it, he felt that resistance by one against a host was vain.

The plunder started. Every article of the little encampment, with the saddle-bags, which he stood upon to protect if possible, was greedily seized. His presence of mind, however, did not forsake him. He calmly meditated for a moment, on what course to take.

Assuming great composure, he went to the chief, and addressing him in Spanish and the few words of Indian he knew, he declared himself to be an American, and demanded if their nation was at war with the Americans. "No," was the reply. "Do you like the Americans?" "Yes — they are our friends." "Where do you get your

spear heads, your blankets?" and so forth, naming
all their foreign articles, one by one. "Get them
from our friends the Americans." "Well, do you
think if you were passing through their nation,
as I am passing through yours, they would rob
you as you have robbed me?" The chief thought
a little, and replied, "No, it would not be right."
Upon which he commanded his people to restore
all the things taken.

Every article of value came back, with the
same dispatch with which it had disappeared,

except the saddle-bags. These, which contained all his money, were necessary for his journey. No one could tell anything of the saddle-bags. Almost in despair of seeing them again, he observed in a thicket at a little distance a squaw, one of the trumpeters, kicking and urging her horse to make him move off, while the intelligent beast would not stir a step from the troop. The General instantly pursued the female robber, and, thanks to her stubborn mustang, secured his property, which was very cunningly hidden under the saddle blanket and herself. The whole squadron then wheeled off, and were seen no more. * * *

When General Austin reached the City of Mexico the new government of Mexico was very unsettled. * * *

After a whole year's delay, at last General Austin had the joy of returning to Texas with the object of his journey fully accomplished. His authority to plant a colony in Texas, under which he had been acting, was confirmed by the new government of Mexico. . . .

In August, when General Austin arrived in the colony, it was nearly broken up, because of his long delay in Mexico, and emigration had totally stopped. Many of the first emigrants had returned to the United States, and a number of those who had started their journey for the colony had stopped in the vicinity of Nacogdoches, or on the Trinity River, and thus the settlement of those sections of the country began.

By hard work and prudent management, however, the life of the expiring colony was soon revived. * * *

— *Mary Austin Holley*

Things to Do

1. One of the best ways to learn about people of long ago is to read stories that were written by persons living at that time. Often the stories sound strange to us. Mrs. Holley told in this story things that actually happened which seem strange to us now.

Explain, in your own words, what she meant when she wrote the following sentences:

a. At his death, Mr. Moses Austin left a request that his son, Stephen F. Austin, should undertake the enterprise which he had thus started, of forming a settlement in Texas.

b. Stephen F. Austin immediately entered upon the prosecution of the enterprise with vigor.

c. By hard work and prudent management, however, the life of the expiring colony was soon revived.

2. Why did Austin have to make an unexpected trip to Mexico City?

3. Why did the trip require great courage and determination?

4. Dramatize the Indian attack on the way to the Mexican capital.

5. In making his claim for the return of his baggage, Austin asked for "fair play." The chief saw the point and agreed with Austin. What does this tell us about the Indian sense of honor?

6. Why do you think that Austin, when in Mexico City, might have given up the whole idea of building a colony in Texas?

7. Try to describe Austin's feelings when he returned after his long, difficult journey and found that his settlement was almost gone.

The Settlers

The cabin stands in the clearing,
The crescent moon rides high;
The green corn grows in tasseled rows
Against the spangled sky.
A rifle shot in the forest,
The hunter's aim is true;
Daddy's brung a turkey cock
For the wedding barbecue.

Light-foot dancers are democrats
In homespun dresses and coon-skin hats;
Lindy Lou in a butternut skirt,
Ezekiel Brown in a hunting shirt,
Nimble toes and thumping heels;
Faster and faster the fiddle squeals.
Tonight we'll dance and tomorrow roam
Into the West to build a new home.

— *James Daugherty*

The Old Three Hundred

In the early days of Texas, people lived far apart. Neighbors seldom saw each other. Chats over the telephone were unheard of and there were no quick visits by automobile! A wedding, or even a funeral, meant that friends could see and visit each other. Noah Smithwick was a settler in Austin's first colony. He tells how the first three hundred colonists in Texas had fun at weddings

They were a social people, these Old Three Hundred. There were a number of weddings and other social gatherings during my short stay in that section, the most notable one perhaps being the marriage of Nicholas McNutt to Miss Cartwright. There were a large number of invited guests, both the families occupying prominent social positions.

Jesse Cartwright, father of the bride, was a man in comfortable circumstances, and himself and family of good breeding. They were among the very first in Austin's colonists, Cartwright being a member of the first ayuntamiento, or town council, organized in Texas.

The bridegroom was a son of a widow McNutt, also among the early arrivals. The

family, **consisting of** mother, two sons, and three
young daughters, came from Louisiana, where
they had been very wealthy, but having suffered
reverses they came to Texas to remake their
fortunes. Bred up in luxury, as they evidently
had been, it was a rough road to fortune they
chose, but they adapted themselves to the situation and made the best of it.

Mrs. McNutt had three brothers, the Welches,
living in Bayou Rapids, La., whom I afterwards
knew. She also had a sister, Mrs. Dr. Peebles,
living with her husband in San Felipe. Dr. Wells
later married a Miss McNutt and Mr. Porter
another.

But to get back to the wedding. Miss Mary Allen, daughter of Martin Allen, a very pretty girl and a great belle, by the way, was bridesmaid, and John McNutt, brother of the bridegroom, was groomsman. There being no priest in the vicinity, Thomas Duke, the "big" alcalde, was summoned from San Felipe. The alcalde tied the knot in good American style, but the contracting parties had in addition, to sign a bond to avail themselves of the priest's services to legalize the marriage at the earliest opportunity.

Among the guests I remember Mrs. [Jane] Long and her daughter Ann, Miss Alcorn, daughter of Elijah Alcorn, Miss Mary, daughter of Moses Shipman, and Mrs. McNutt and daughters, none of the latter then grown, Captain Martin Elliot, and John Alcorn.

After the first and most important number on the program was carried out, the next thing in order was the wedding supper, which was the best the market afforded. That being disposed of, the floor was cleared for dancing. It mattered not that the floors were made of puncheons. When young folks danced those days they danced; they didn't glide around. They "shuffled" and "double shuffled," "wired," and "cut the pigeon's wing," making the splinters fly.

There were some of the boys, however, who were not provided with shoes, and moccasins

were not adapted to that kind of dancing floor, and moreover they couldn't make noise enough, but their more fortunate brethren were not disposed to put on airs, so, when they had danced a turn, they generously exchanged foot gear with those wearing moccasins and gave them the ring, and we just literally kicked every splinter off that floor before morning. The fiddle, played by Jesse Thompson's man Mose, being rather too weak to make itself heard above the din of clattering feet, we had in another fellow with a clevis and pin to strengthen the orchestra, and we had a most enjoyable time.

Another dancing party in which I participated was at Martin Varner's, near Columbia. When we were all assembled and ready to begin business, it was found that Mose, the only fiddler around, had failed to come, so we called in an old darky belonging to Colonel Zeno Philips, who performed on a clevis as an accompaniment to his singing, while another Negro scraped on a cotton hoe with a case knife. The favorite chorus was,

"O git up gals in de mawnin',
O git up gals in de mawnin',
O git up gals in de mawnin',
Jes at de break ob day."

At the conclusion, the performer gave an extra blow to the clevis, while the dancers responded with a series of skillful rat-tat-tats with heel and toe.

— *Noah Smithwick*

Things to Do

1. Who were the Old Three Hundred?
2. Do you know people who are descended from them?
3. Why were weddings such fun-making occasions?
4. Compare dancing and dance music then and now.
5. How old must Noah Smithwick have been when he wrote this story?

6. Discuss the meaning of the expressions below:
   a. families occupying prominent social positions
   b. a man in comfortable circumstances
   c. but having suffered reverses, they came to Texas to remake their fortunes
   d. above the din of clattering feet
   e. gave an extra blow on the clevis

The Plowman

Where the mould-board turns the forest loam
In the new-made clearing we'll make our home,
With a bull-tongue plow and a broad-blade axe
With straining oxen and bending backs.
By the grey rail fence round the laughing corn
Men sing at their work in the early morn.
The corn shocks tell of a bumper year
For tall strong sons of the free frontier.

Red-skin warriors behind the screen
Of mountain laurel in forest green,
Across the clearing an arrow flies
As savage yells from the bushes rise.
The settlers flee to the log stockade
Where men and women are unafraid,
Though danger or peril is lurking near
On the perilous paths of the pioneer.

— *James Daugherty*

Experiences in Early Texas

The author of this story was the wife of Robert J. Kleberg, Sr., who fought in the battle of San Jacinto, and the great-grandmother of Bob Kleberg, the present manager of the King Ranch. She told the story in German to her grandson, Rudolph Kleberg, Jr., who translated it into English. She came from Germany to Texas, along with relatives, in 1834. Some of her relatives had already come to explore the country, and had settled at Cat Spring, Austin County.

Upon arriving at our place at Cat Spring, we moved into a big log house which my husband and brothers had built. There was neither floor nor ceiling to it, and in the only room was a big fire-place. As soon, however, as the most important field work was done, the men built an extra fine house for our parents. This had a floor and ceilings of logs.

We had most of our goods in common. When we decided to go to Texas, we put all our savings in a common treasury, part of which we invested in buying things we thought necessary to start a settlement. Our intention was to buy a tract of land and later locate our individual claims. It did not work out well, and after the war it broke up.

Circumstances were different from our expectations. My brothers had pictured pioneer life as one of hunting and fishing, of freedom from the restraints of Prussian society. It was hard for them to settle down to the drudgery of splitting rails and cultivating the fields, work which was entirely new to them.

The settlers with whom we came in contact were very kind and hospitable. They would receive one with genuine pleasure and share the last piece of bread. Money was out of the question. If you had offered it to those people, they would have been amazed. When you came to one of the old settlers, you were expected to make yourself at home. He would see that your horses were well fed and offered you the best cheer that he could, and you were expected to do the same when the next opportunity presented itself.

In the main everything was very quiet and peaceful, but there was a great dissatisfaction with the Mexican government. Settlers were constantly saying that since the Mexicans gave them no government, they could not see why they could not have a government of their own and be rid of the Mexicans.

We lived about ten miles from San Felipe, where there were from two to four stores, besides a tavern and saloon and from thirty to forty private houses. In the stores you could buy almost anything you wanted in those days, but of course the prices were high. There were no churches but plenty of camp meetings, one of which I attended. There was considerable trade in cotton and cattle in San Felipe and San Antonio.

Old Colonel Pettus brought us the first news of the beginning of the war. The unmarried men of our party then joined the march to San Antonio and helped capture that city.

. . . Things were now quiet for a while, and everybody began to work once more. But when the news of the fall of the Alamo came, there was great excitement. Some of the people wanted to leave Texas altogether. There was quite a debate in our family as to what course it was most advisable to pursue, until my husband was seconded in his views by my father. And so it was finally decided that my father should stay with us, while my husband and brothers were to join the army.

As the men left, their families began to move, intending to cross the Sabine River; and we set out like the rest.[1] As we passed through San Felipe my husband and my brother, Louis von Roeder, left us to join Houston's army. Having only one big ox wagon, and being compelled to take in it four families and their baggage, we left behind much that was valuable. My father and I drove our cattle and pack horses; and I carried my daughter Clara, who was then a child of a few months, upon the saddle in front of me.

Most of the families traveled separately until they reached the Brazos, where all were compelled to come to a halt. It was necessary to drive the cattle across before the people could pass over; and this was attended with a good deal of difficulty. From forty to fifty families were trying to cross with their cattle, and the noise and confusion were terrible. There was only one small ferryboat, which carried a wagon

---

[1] Known as "The Runaway Scrape."

34

and a few passengers.   Many of the people were on foot.

The next morning after crossing the Brazos we stopped at "Cow" Cooper's, called thus from the large number of cattle he owned. Cooper told the people to help themselves to all the meat he had, since he did not want the Mexicans to have it.   The people kept together for about a day, after which they again separated. We camped near the Clear Creek, where young Louis von Roeder was born in a corn crib.

We intended to remain here as long as possible on account of my sister.   During the night, however, my brother, Otto von Roeder, came to tell us that the Mexicans had gone to the crossing below San Felipe and that we must move on. And so we once more set out, being compelled to stop again after the second day. We camped in the neighborhood of a house where a number of families had collected. Here we heard the sound of cannon, and the next morning came an old man, Georgens by name, whom we knew quite well. He told us that the battle had been fought.[1] When my father asked him about the result he told us that he had stayed with the army until he saw that everybody was thoroughly engaged, whereupon he decided that they were able to get on without him, and he left.

On the afternoon of the same day, we learned the result of the battle of San Jacinto. We did not believe the good news until we heard it confirmed by the young men whom we had sent to ascertain the truth of the report.

It was our intention to return home; but we heard that the Indians were in the country, and so we followed the example of the families who were with us and went to Galveston Island. There were also a number of Mexican prisoners who were kept on the island by the Texan government. We received some supplies from the people of the United States, but we never-

[1]Battle of San Jacinto.

36

theless here passed through some of our hardest experiences. Many of us were sick, and though there was a physician, Dr. Jaeger, among us, who generously gave his services, yet he had no medicines. My sister-in-law, Ottilie von Roeder, died here, and we buried her under the Three Lone Trees.

My husband and brother Louis, who had both been in the Texas army all during this time, joined us here, and we first intended to remain permanently. But it was evident that this was impossible, and we decided to return to Cat Spring. When we came home we found everything we had left was gone. We had buried our books, but the place had been found and they were torn to pieces. We had to begin anew, and with less than we had when we started.

— *Rosa Kleberg*

Things to Do

1. Discuss the following with your classmates:
   a. Compare Mrs. Kleberg's ideas of what living in Texas would be like with the conditions she actually found.
   b. Why were the settlers especially kind and considerate to new families?
   c. Where did the Klebergs live in Texas?
   d. When the news of the fall of the Alamo came, what did the Klebergs do?
   e. Why did "Cow" Cooper give his cattle to the people?
   f. Where were the Klebergs when the news came of the Battle of San Jacinto?
   g. The Klebergs went to Galveston Island after the war: why did they wish to leave Galveston?
2. Perhaps there are elderly people in your community who could tell interesting stories of their early experiences. Decide who these people are and have members of your class plan to interview them to hear the stories. If you live near King Ranch, you might be able to interview Mrs. Kleberg's great-grandson, Bob Kleberg.

A Pioneer Thanksgiving in Texas

This play was made from a true story of a pioneer Thanksgiving in Texas. The story was told by a descendant of the Vincent family.

Characters

IKE VINCENT

MARY VINCENT, *his wife*

JOHN VINCENT, *their twelve year old son*

MARY ETTA VINCENT, *their ten year old daughter*

BETSY, *large Negro mammy and cook for the Vincents*

INDIANS, *including three men, two squaws, and two small children*

TIME: *Thanksgiving morning, 1850*

SETTING: *Combined dining room and kitchen of the Vincent pioneer home, with bedroom adjoining. The two separated by a partition through which a small peephole or window is placed.*

AT RISE OF CURTAIN: *Mrs. Vincent getting silverware and plates out of closet. Betsy at fireplace cooking. Calendar on wall showing year 1850 in large figures. Ike Vincent drying hands on towel, John at wash basin washing hands. Mary Etta at center playing with doll.*

VINCENT: My! but that cooking smells good. That old Thanksgiving smell is in the air.

JOHN: I'm hungry too. Those turkeys I killed were heavy. Bet they weighed twenty pounds each.

VINCENT: That deer I brought in from the morning hunt weighed a hundred pounds, from the way it felt. Is the venison all sliced, Betsy?

BETSY: Yes sah, Mr. Vincent. All ready for you to broil.

MRS. VINCENT: Well, we have much to be thankful for. A new log house in the new state of Texas. It's hard to believe that six months ago we were still in Virginia. And so far the Indians haven't bothered us, although we were warned to watch out.

VINCENT: Yes, it *was* a long move we made, and we've all worked hard. And I'm in the mood to celebrate.

JOHN: How long before we eat, Betsy?

BETSY: Now, go long, you hungry boy. You're hollow clear down to the tips o' your toes. It'll be another thirty minutes yet.

VINCENT: That'll give us time to feed and water the horses. Come on, John, you can help.

MRS. VINCENT: Better get back sooner if you can, Ike. We're depending on you to broil the venison, you know.

VINCENT: All right, Mary. We're off to the barn (*Exit Vincent and John*).

MRS. VINCENT: (*Looking around and pointing as she names foods*) Let's see. The yellow yams are in the ashes, getting brown. A pot of beans seasoned with side meat is on one end of the crane —

MARY ETTA: (*Going close to crane and looking*) An iron pot with white potatoes is boiling in the other end—

BETSY: A journey cake is brownin' on the hearth, and biscuits are baking in the three-legged skillet.

MRS. VINCENT: And Ike's venison is sliced and ready to broil. And the turkeys are roasting in the oven. And the gravy is made. Yes, I guess we will dine right well today. Now Mary Etta, you can get out the knives and forks, while I clear off the table and get it ready to set (*They work a while*).

MARY ETTA: But mother! We don't have any fruit cake! And how can we be thankful without one?

MRS. VINCENT: Never mind, daughter. We can't have everything. And I'm sure we will have the best turkey and venison that any family ever had.

MARY ETTA: (*Pouting*) But I want some fruit cake!

41

BETSY: Now you jus' get that grumble out o' your pretty mouf, honey chile. Ol' Betsy got a surprise. (*Goes over to a narrow bed in corner of room and with grunting and mumbling gets down on knees. Reaches far under bed and pulls out bundle*).

MARY ETTA: Why that's the bundle with the secret in it. And you wouldn't tell any of us what was in it.

BETSY: Yes'm, that's it (*Removes several layers of cloth, while others watch. Finally a cheese tub comes to view*).

MRS. VINCENT: Cheese! How thoughtful! Bless your dear old heart, Betsy, you—

BETSY: No, ma'am, that's not it. Here it is (*Lifts out a huge fruit cake*).

MARY ETTA: A fruit cake! A big, beautiful, sweet, brown fruit cake!

BETSY: (*Turning out the cake and placing it on shelf*) Yes'm. Me and that cake really had a time, back in Virginia when I was a gettin' it made, and on the road to Texas. But we got here, both of us.

MARY ETTA: Now if Father and John would only hurry back from the barn. I'm getting hungry!

MRS. VINCENT: Hush, daughter. They haven't had time yet. They will be ·back before long.

BETSY: (*Looks out of door. Drops pan on floor and gasps. A look of horror on face. In loud whisper*) Lawd help us!

MRS. VINCENT: What's the matter, Betsy? You look scared. (*Looks out of door*) Indians! And in their war paint!

MARY ETTA: And they're coming to the house!

MRS. VINCENT: We'll have to go into the bedroom and close the door. It's the only place we can go.

MARY ETTA: But our Thanksgiving dinner! And the fruit cake!

MRS. VINCENT: Hurry! There's no time to lose! They're coming, and they'll see us! (*Hustles Betsy and Mary Etta through the door and locks it, then the three watch through small window or peephole*).

INDIANS: (*Come up to door from outside, look in, and slowly enter. Stand looking around uncertainly*).

INDIAN MAN: Ugh! (*He and other Indians begin to move about, examining things. Much pantomime and motioning between them. Finally one of them discovers a turkey and motions to others, and all begin to eat*).

MRS. VINCENT: There goes John's turkey. And they're eating it with their fingers!

INDIAN SQUAW: Ugh! (*Goes poking about in kitchen, finally finding journey cake. Picks it up, breaks into pieces, and gives pieces to others*).

MARY ETTA: (*In loud whisper*) They're eating Betsy's journey cake. (*Aloud*) Oh-h!

MRS. VINCENT: Shh! (*Claps hand over Mary Etta's mouth and motions toward Indians, then takes hand away. Mary Etta nods*).

INDIAN CHILDREN: Ugh! (*Discover fruit cake and begin removing wrappings. One of them digs fingers into it*).

BETSY: The little heathens! They're not goin' to eat that beautiful fruit cake that I brought

44

all the way from Virginia. (*Grabs sheet from
bed and wraps it around her. Grabs John's
pair of stilts from corner of room, mounts
them, pushes door open, and starts into
kitchen. Mrs. Vincent tries to prevent her
from going, but she goes anyhow. Enters
kitchen on stilts shouting*) Yow! Whoopee!
(*Lets loose handle of one stilt, which comes
down on head of Indian man. Falls on another Indian, mashing him to floor*).

ALL THE INDIANS BUT ONE CHILD: Ugh! Ugh! Ugh!
(*Flee from house pell mell. One little Indian hides under table*).

BETSY: (*Picks self up from floor and painfully rises, groaning*) Oh-h! I think I broke my leg. But I taught 'em a good lesson.

MRS. VINCENT: I should say you did! And I doubt if they all recover. That was a real blow you gave one of them. I would hate for 223 pounds to fall on me, not to mention a stilt.

BETSY: Serves 'em right for tryin' to eat up our Thanksgivin' dinner. I could have stood it if it hadn't been for that fruit cake. But I worked on it too hard to stand by and watch 'em gobble it up.

VINCENT: (*Bursting in at door, followed by John*). Mary! Betsy! What on earth has happened?

MRS. VINCENT: Too late, Ike. Betsy has just routed a tribe of Indians, single handed, and with no weapons but a pair of stilts and a bed sheet.

VINCENT: I heard a bang so loud I thought the house was being torn down; then I saw Indians running in every direction. I wondered if Old Nick was after them.

BETSY: Not Old Nick. It was a ghost.

MRS. VINCENT: Well, it's over and I don't think they'll come back. And maybe we still have enough left to eat.

INDIAN CHILD: (*From under table*) Wow! Wow! Wow!

VINCENT: (*Looks under table, revealing papoose*). Well, bless my soul! His mammy and daddy ran off and left him. And he's been in the molasses, and it's all over him!

MRS. VINCENT: Mary Etta, get one of your dresses and put it on him. And, John, while she's getting the dress, take him outside and wash him. (*Exit John with child, and Mary Etta into bedroom. She returns with dress and goes outside*).

MRS. VINCENT: (*Looking around*) Now, let's see what's left. One of the turkeys is still untouched. And the biscuits are still unharmed in the skillet. Betsy, you will have to mix another journey cake.

BETSY: Yes, ma'am, I'll do that in a jiffy (*Goes to work*).

VINCENT: (*Poking about*) Here's the venison, still sliced and ready to be broiled. Guess that's my job (*Goes to work*).

MRS. VINCENT: And I'll clear up the table, set it, and put on the food that's already cooked. (*Goes to work*).

MARY ETTA: (*Enters, carrying Indian papoose, who is asleep*) He went sound asleep by the time we had him dressed.

MRS. VINCENT: Take him into the other room, put him on your bed, and cover him up. I imagine his mother will be back for him after a while (*Exit Mary Etta. She returns presently without the child and helps her mother with the table and dishes. After two or three minutes of this*).

MRS. VINCENT: Ready, Betsy?

BETSY: Yes ma'am. The journey cake's done to a turn.

MRS. VINCENT: Ready, Ike?

VINCENT: Ready. This venison's broiled to exactly the right shade, with the juice running out.

MRS. VINCENT: Ready, John?

JOHN: As soon as I wash my hands. And I want some of the white meat of that turkey.

MRS. VINCENT: You shall have it. Ready, Mary Etta?

MARY ETTA: Yes, mother. And I want a l-a-r-g-e slice of the fruit cake.

MRS. VINCENT: Then everyone come to the table (*They gather around it standing*). Ike, will you ask the blessing?

VINCENT: Let's make it a silent blessing, and let's all have a hand. For we have much to be thankful for this day.

ALL: (*Bow their heads and remain quiet as*)
CURTAIN
— *Elise Biles* (*As told to J. A. Rickard*)

Things to Do

1. Plan to use this play at Thanksgiving. Have try-outs for each character by assigning different pupils to read the parts. Choose the characters for the final production on the basis of clear, accurate, expressive reading. A good actor or actress makes characters "live" for the audience.

2. Invite another class to see your play.

3. You may write other plays about Thanksgiving. You could use the original Thanksgiving story or experiences of your family. Your class could present a group of plays for Thanksgiving — your own as well as the ones you have read.

Fighting for Freedom

Going to Texas

Many people in many places have heard glowing stories of Texas and have longed for a chance to visit it. Over a century ago, a young native of Kentucky, John C. Duval, heard of a country of broad prairies covered with droves of buffaloes and wild horses. The Texas War for Independence gave him a chance to come to Texas. He was one of a few prisoners at Goliad who escaped the massacre by bolting as they were fired upon by the Mexican soldiers.

In 1835 the people of Texas, or rather the settlers from the "States", determined to throw off the Mexican yoke, and resist to the end any further trampling upon their liberties. At that time, with the exception of Mexicans and Indians, there were probably not more than twenty thousand people in the colonies. Although the Mexican government for several years previously had refused to respect the rights and privileges guaranteed them under the constitution of 1824, I hardly think the colonists with their limited means and numbers would have ventured to rebel against Mexico, if they had not felt sure of help from their friends and comrades in the

United States. They were not disappointed.
Many young men from almost every state in the
Union, armed and equipped at their own expense,
hastened to the aid of the colonists as soon as
the revolution began.

A volunteer company was organized for
this purpose in my native village, and although
I was scarcely old enough to bear arms, I resolved to join it. But it was due to no wish for
"military fame" that led me to do so. One of
the frequent visitors at my father's house was an
old friend of his who had been in Texas and
traveled over a considerable portion of it, and
who afterward held a position in the cabinet of

the first president. He was enthusiastic in his praise of the country, and without reason a great longing sprang up in my bosom to see for myself the "broad prairies", the beautiful streams and vast herds of buffaloes and wild horses of which he had so often given me glowing descriptions. By joining this company I thought an opportunity would be given me of satisfying a desire which perhaps might never again offer itself; and so, in spite of the opposition of relatives and friends, my name was added to the company roll.

I purchased a good Kentucky rifle (with the use of which I was already well acquainted), shot pouch, powder horn, tomahawk, and butcher knife, and thus equipped, with my knapsack on my shoulders, I fell into ranks; and amid the waving of handkerchiefs and the cheering of bystanders I bid adieu to my native village and started for the "promised land" of Texas.

— John C. Duval

Things to Do

1. Why did Duval think Texas might not have rebelled against Mexico without the hope of aid from the United States?
2. Why did he decide to aid Texas?
3. What equipment did he take along?
4. Sketch a picture of Duval as he said good-by to his native village and started for the "promised land" of Texas. Re-reading the last paragraph of the story should help you in making the picture.

Davy Crockett in Texas

Davy Crockett was born soon after the American Revolution in the wild river country of East Tennessee. With the Indians often on the warpath and the woods full of wild animals, Davy knew that he must become a great hunter. Later he felt that the people of his state should be well represented in Washington, so he went to Congress for three terms. Finally, the great western country beckoned him. Taking his famous musket, he started for Texas. In this, as in other decisions he made, he followed the advice in the famous motto which he gave to the world — "Be sure you're right, then go ahead."

After hours of delay, the Arkansas River steamboat, sending black clouds from her smokestack, at last drew up to the docks with a whistle and a clang of bells. A crowd was on hand to meet her, and more than one person noted the tall stranger who strode ashore.

A striking figure, he made his way to the nearest hotel. The tail of his coonskin cap bobbed against his leather hunting shirt, both garments in keeping with the long rifle cradled in the crook of his left arm.

People of Little Rock in 1835 were used to
hunters, but this man was unusual. Guests kept
watching him, even after he had sat down with
others at the dining room table. One nudged
his companion.

"His picture's on a presidential campaign
leaflet. He was a congressman from Tennessee
— was against Jackson."

The other man nodded. "That's right —
David Crockett!"

Before long everyone in the room knew
who the stranger was, and all tried to make him
welcome.

They gave a banquet in his honor. They
held a shooting match during which he displayed

his marksmanship with the rifle, "Betsy." Though they asked him to stay in Arkansas to go "b'ar huntin'," he shook his head.

"I'd like to," he told them, "but I'm goin' to Texas. Things are happenin' in Texas. I must go there. You know my motto: 'Be sure you're right, then go ahead.' Well, I'm goin'."

He had traveled by water from Tennessee, but now he needed a horse. Though his new friends would not go to Texas with him, as he wanted them to do, they furnished him a mount and several traveled with him for fifty miles or more.

As Crockett and his friends approached the bank of the Ouachita River, they heard a violin.

The musician, a gray-whiskered man sitting in a cart in midstream, was playing the instrument as if he were "high and dry."

"You've missed the ford," one of the men shouted to him.

"I know it," he replied.

"If you go ten feet farther, you'll be drowned!"

"That I know, too."

"Turn back," another one of Crockett's companions called.

"I can't," the old man answered.

"Then how'll you get out?"

"Don't know." Just as he began playing again, Crockett rode out, caught the horse's reins, turned him around, and led the traveler, a preacher, back to shore.

"I have no money to pay you, but I'll preach you a sermon," he offered.

"No, thanks!" Two or three of the men exclaimed this so quickly it brought a smile to Crockett's face.

"These men are headin' back to Little Rock. I'm goin' to Texas," declared Crockett. "Want to come along?"

"I'll go part way — to the turn-off to the Ozarks."

If we are to believe the story, the preacher continued playing his violin, Crockett sang, and

the two headed for Fulton, a famous crossing of the Red River near the Texas line. His companion who traveled with him for a day, explained that he played the violin when he was in trouble.

"I could have yelled for help till I was hoarse," he explained, "and I might've been there yet. But folks listen when they hear music."

At Fulton, Crockett asked many questions about Texas. He met some people going toward Little Rock and asked them to take back to his Arkansas friends the horse he had been riding, with his sincere thanks. Then he bought one of his own and set out to explore that part of

Texas nearest to him.

It is impossible to trace all of Crockett's movements, but it is known that he left Little Rock on November 12, 1835, and that he reached Nacogdoches, Texas, on January 5, 1836. During the time between these dates — almost two months — he apparently saw much of the new country. He went over most of Red River County and visited in Clarksville. He may have pushed out as far as the headwaters of the east fork of the Trinity River, stopping at a place which later was called Honey Grove.

Crockett was evidently pleased. He wrote to relatives in Tennessee that Texas was the finest country he had seen and that he planned to secure land in an attractive location in the Red River Valley.

He then rode back to Fulton, boarded a small steamer, and went down the Red River to Natchitoches, Louisiana. At one of these two places other men joined him. The group became known as "Crockett's Company."

From Natchitoches, Crockett and his friends rode on to Nacogdoches. In some way the news of his coming had gone ahead of him, and he was greeted with booming cannon.

"I guess that means welcome," he commented, "as long as they don't point the guns toward us." It did mean welcome, as did a ban-

quet given in his honor.

At Nacogdoches he took an oath which read, "I will be true to any future republican government that may hereafter be declared." He was now a Texan!

After spending several days at Nacogdoches and at San Augustine, he and his friends pushed farther into Texas. They stopped for awhile at Washington-on-the-Brazos, where independence was soon to be declared.

Crockett stopped next at Gay Hill, ten miles northwest of present Brenham, at the home of John M. Swisher, who later wrote the following account of his visit:

. . .It happened that on the day that Colonel Crockett arrived I had been out hunting with a party of friends. I had killed my second, and I believe, my last deer, which I tied behind my saddle. I reached home with it about nightfall. Colonel Crockett surprised me by coming out and assisting me in taking it down from the horse. He complimented me highly by calling me his young hunter, and bantering me to a shooting match. I accepted this proposition, since he offered to shoot off hand and give me a rest. My pride swelled at once. I would not have changed places with the President himself. We tried our skill with the rifle every day he remained with us.

His rifle I well remember. It was ornamented with a silver plate set into the stock, upon which was engraved "David Crockett." He called it "Betsy."

At the time I saw Colonel Crockett, I judge him to have been forty years old. He was stout and muscular, about six feet in height, and weighed from one hundred and eighty to two hundred pounds. He was of a florid complexion, with intelligent gray eyes. He had small side-whiskers, inclining to sandy. His countenance, although firm and determined, wore a pleasant expression.

He was fond of talking, and had an ease and grace about him that rendered him irresistible. During his stay at my father's it was a rare occurrence for any of us to get to bed before twelve or one o'clock. He told us a great many anecdotes. Many of them were commonplace and amounted to nothing in themselves, but his inimitable way of telling them would convulse one with laughter.

I shall never forget the day he left us for San Antonio. We watched him as he rode away by the side of his young traveling companion (B. A. M. Smith) with feelings of admiration and regret. We little thought how soon he was to perish — a martyr to the cause of liberty.

Somewhere in Texas, David Crockett became separated from his friends when they gave chase to a herd of buffaloes. Nightfall found him alone on a broad expanse of level ground covered with mesquite and cactus.

In looking for a place to spend the night he stopped his horse under a large tree and dismounted. At this moment Crockett heard a terrifying roar above him and looked up in time to see a Mexican mountain lion crouched to spring at him.

Quickly raising his rifle, he fired directly at

the head of the animal. This seemed only to
infuriate the lion who leaped from the tree, landing close to David. Swinging his rifle as a club,
Crockett struck the animal with all his might,
but this only caused him to charge furiously upon
David, knocking him to the ground.

The lion's teeth were gnawing into his shoulder, and David knew he was in a life and death
struggle. With his one free hand he seized his
hunting knife and plunged the blade deep into
the heart of the lion. The lion gasped, quivered,
and rolled over dead.

Crockett was weak and almost exhausted.
Scraping together enough leaves and twigs, he
made a bed for the night.

The next morning while looking for his horse which had wandered off, he suddenly found himself in the presence of a group of Indians who had approached unseen. Luckily it turned out that they were friendly and not only furnished Crockett a horse to ride but also helped him find his friends.

Crockett's companions were overjoyed to see him for they had almost given him up as lost.

There are strange stories about the men who went with Crockett to San Antonio. One was a gambler called Thimblerig, whom Crockett had outwitted on the river boat, but who, nevertheless, became his devoted follower. Another, a romantic young man known as Bee Hunter, had a sweetheart in Nacogdoches. A third was a former pirate; a fourth, an Indian, whom Crockett had given a helping hand.

How many of these actually existed is not certain, but it is known that he had friends and followers when he reached San Antonio, an old town of fewer than two thousand people, and at that time held by a small company of Texas soldiers. However, it was an important place. For more than a hundred years it had been in the hands of the Spanish and the Mexicans, and was regarded as the key or gateway to Texas.

The heart of the defense of San Antonio was the Alamo, an old mission and fort established by the Franciscan Missionaries early in the eighteenth century.

Commanded by General Cos, a brother-in-law of General Santa Anna, a Mexican army had been in control of the city until December 10, 1835. Although the Mexican forces numbered about 1,300 against 300, the Texans had penned the general and his men in the Alamo. Because they were in danger of starving, they had surrendered and had been set free on their promise not to fight again against the Texans.

Santa Anna was enraged at the defeat of his brother-in-law.

"I'll have revenge on those upstart Texans," he is said to have declared. Certain it is that early in 1836 he was making extensive plans to invade Texas. And, according to all rumors, he was heading for San Antonio.

When Crockett reached that town, he and his friends found a band of fewer than 150 men stationed at the Alamo. General Houston, who had been appointed commander of the Texas forces, had sent a messenger ordering the troops to retreat — an order that was delivered about the middle of January.

Houston believed that it would not be possible to hold the place with such a small force. Events proved that he was right. When Bowie arrived to deliver the order to retreat, he de-

cided it would not do to abandon the Alamo. He wrote, "We had rather die in these ditches than give it up to the enemy."

William B. Travis, a young lawyer who took command after Bowie became ill, also favored holding the fortress. The commanding officers reasoned that if a mere handful of Texans could defeat and capture General Cos, they could as easily defeat Santa Anna.

Crockett agreed with Bowie and Travis. His opinion may have been based in part on his dislike of Houston, for, in Tennessee, Houston had been a friend and Crockett a foe of President Jackson. The other men at the Alamo seemed to feel that the only honorable course was to defend the fortress, rather than abandon it without a fight.

Bowie was now ill, and Travis was in command. One authority stated that the command was offered to Crockett. It was also reported that Crockett offered to go elsewhere for help but that Travis wanted him to remain at the Alamo. Travis, in one of his letters, wrote, "Colonel Crockett was seen at all points, inspiring the men to do their duty."

The Mexican army slowly approached San Antonio in regular formation, the men marching and the officers riding gaily decorated horses.

For several days the Mexicans bombarded the Alamo from a distance, but the cannon balls made little impression on its thick walls. On the night of February 24, Travis sent out his famous appeal for help, an appeal in which he asked for quick aid. He declared that he would never surrender or retreat, and just before he signed his name he wrote, VICTORY OR DEATH.

A few brave souls answered his appeal. Thirty-two came from Gonzales, but Colonel Fannin at Goliad did not arrive with troops.

The end of the siege came on Sunday morning, March 6. Santa Anna's forces, now swelled to several thousand men, stormed the Alamo and killed the last of its defenders. Per-

"Colonel Crockett was seen at all points, inspiring the men to do their duty."

haps fewer than half a dozen, including a woman, a child, and a Negro slave, lived to tell the story.

There are varying tales as to the role of Crockett in the siege. One account says that Travis was killed early in the fighting, that J. J. Baugh next in charge was also killed, and that Crockett took command. This source of information says that his body was found inside the Alamo, that he had a knife in his hand, and that the bodies of twenty-two of the enemy lay near him.

Another story says that he and four other Texans were captured and later slain, but this is generally disbelieved.

Mrs. Dickinson, one of the few whose lives were spared, wrote the following account:[1]

> I knew Colonels Crockett, Bowie, and Travis well. Colonel Crockett was a performer on the violin, and often during the siege took it up and played his favorite tunes.
>
> I heard him say several times during the eleven days of the siege: "I think we had better march out and die in the open air. I don't like to be hemmed up."
>
> * * * At this moment a Mexican officer came into the room, and addressing me in English, asked, "Are you Mrs. Dickinson?" I answered, "Yes." Then he said, "If you

[1]*History of Texas*, by J. M. Morphis, p. 174 (1875).

68

wish to save your life, follow me." I followed him, and although shot at and wounded, was spared.

As we passed through the enclosed ground in front of the church, I saw heaps of dead and dying . . .

I recognized Colonel Crockett lying dead and mutilated between the church and the two story barrack building, and even remember seeing his peculiar cap lying by his side. * * *

The real story of Crockett's actual work will never be known, but we may be sure that he died bravely, as did the other martyrs of the Alamo. History records no braver deeds than those of the defenders of that fortress.

The news of the tragedy at San Antonio made headlines in the newspapers of the United States.

For twenty years after his death, stories were told about Crockett as if he were alive. Some said he was shot by a silver bullet, which left no trace or wound. Others said he had not really been killed at the Alamo, but had escaped. They created a fabulous hero, doing such deeds as no other man had ever done.

The people of Texas remember him in a different way. To them he is a real hero, not a hero of "tall tales." They placed his name on both the old and the new monuments to the heroes of the Alamo on the capitol grounds at Austin.

Yes, Texans feel differently about Crockett. To them he is not only a singer of songs, a fabulous hunter, and a matchless woodsman. He is a hero of the Alamo. Wherever patriotic Texans assemble, his name is spoken with reverence.

— *J. A. Rickard*
Clyde Inez Martin

Things to Do

1. Choose members of your group to read aloud the following parts of the story:
   a. Crockett in Arkansas.
   b. The man with the violin.
   c. Days in East Texas.
   d. Natchitoches to Nacogdoches.
   e. At San Augustine.
   f. Visit at Gay Hill.
   g. The mountain lion.
   h. The Alamo.
2. Share with your classmates other stories you have heard about Davy Crockett.
3. What was Davy Crockett's motto?
4. You would probably enjoy reading the biography of Crockett by Constance Rourke. Your teacher might like to read it aloud to your group.

He located the ship before nightfall

The Horse Marines

Many of us have heard the old song which begins:

I'm Captain Jenks of the horse marines,
I feed my horse on corn and beans,
And swing the ladies in their teens,
For this is the style of the army.

Perhaps the song is just a jolly rhyme for parties, but it does have a historical background. The "Captain Jenks" of Texas history is Major Isaac W. Burton, who commanded horse marines in a battle, not at a dance.

The Texans were rebelling against the Mexican government in 1836, and had already fought and won the important battle of San Jacinto, a battle which finally gave them independence.

But the war was not over, so when on May 29, Burton was ordered to scout the Texas Gulf Coast as far south as Refugio, he hastened with twenty well-mounted and armed men to obey the command.

Four days later he heard that a strange looking vessel was anchored in Copano Bay, not far from Refugio. He located the ship before nightfall, stationed his patrol on the beach, and the next morning signaled the vessel to send a boat ashore. Whether the order was obeyed through fear, or curiosity, or for some other reason is not known, but obeyed it was. Five of the enemy were landed, and they were promptly seized and made prisoners.

At once sixteen of the horsemen left their mounts, set forth in the boat, and boarded and captured the vessel, the *Watchman*. They found it loaded with provisions intended for the Mexican army, which had been defeated a short time earlier.

Then contrary winds arose, and the sailing of the vessel was delayed until June 17. This was fortunate, for two more, the *Comanche* and the *Fanny Butler,* also anchored and were captured. The captain of the *Watchman* was forced to invite the captains of the new arrivals aboard, where the Horse Marines promptly made them prisoners — a clever trick!

Altogether, the three ships were carrying about $25,000 worth of provisions, a windfall, a prize indeed, for the Texas army. How the twenty men and their horses managed finally to deliver the ships safely to Port Lavaca is not clear, but it is believed that they used their horses somehow in the process.

At any rate, they became known as the Horse Marines.

Things to Do

1. If the independence of Texas had been won at San Jacinto, why were the Mexicans still sending aid to their army?
2. How was it possible for a group of twenty Texans on horses to capture three ships?
3. What is your opinion of the title of this story?
4. Why were the provisions of the three ships a windfall to the Texas army? Can you give examples of windfalls that have happened to you or your friends?

A Texas Boy Hero

Fishing tackle and bait ready at last, John Hill waited impatiently while his older brothers, Jeff and James Monroe, finished their game of pitching horseshoes. If they hurried, there would still be time to go as far as the deep pool —

"Hey! Somebody's coming!" Jeff cried out excitedly. They watched intently as a horseman circled the house and rode toward the barn. Then — their fishing trip forgotten — the boys hurried across the back yard to the rider who had stopped and was talking to their father.

They heard him ask, "Is it the Indians?"

"No, it's the Mexicans," the rider replied. "They've captured San Antonio and taken several hundred prisoners. Captain Jack Hays is at Seguin getting together a force to drive them out. Can we count on you, Mr. Hill?"

"That you can, and one or two of my boys. I thought we licked them at San Jacinto, but it seems they are trying it again."

John asked, "Father, may I go?"

"No, Son, youngsters don't need to be in war."

"But I made that trip to Austin alone, to have those deeds recorded. That was dangerous; you said so yourself. And I could take care of you and Jeff. James Monroe could stay with Mother."

Asa Hill looked thoughtfully at his oldest son, who had started back to the house. "Yes, he has not been well since he was in that San Jacinto campaign. You ought to stay too, John, but let's wait and talk to Mother."

At first, John's mother would not give her consent, but when the boy begged hard to go along "to take care of father and Jeff," she finally agreed.

James Monroe gave John his rifle. "It's the right size for you. I used it at San Jacinto," he told him. "You must never let it fall into the hands of an enemy, though. Promise?"

"I promise," John replied, clutching the rifle fondly.

Early the next morning the father and his two youngest sons started, John riding his pony, with the rifle tied to his saddle. They rode to La Grange, where three other boys, all under sixteen but older than John, joined them. John was glad to have them along: he did not feel so small with them near.

General Adrian Woll had just invaded Texas and captured San Antonio, but he was gone before Captain Hays could follow him. However, Captain Nicholas Dawson, with fifty men, had left La Grange about twelve hours before Asa Hill and his two boys arrived. Dawson and his men had been cut off and massacred near the Salado River, about six miles from San Antonio.

Indeed, Woll's invasion was not the first one. General Vásquez, with another Mexican army, had descended on the town in March, six months earlier. He too had left, but he had taken some prisoners with him across the Rio Grande. Texans no longer felt safe. They demanded angrily that something be done to stop these raids.

The Texas volunteers, including the Hills, went on from La Grange to San Antonio, where they camped at Mission Concepción. Early in October, President Houston of Texas ordered General Alexander Somervell to organize an army of volunteers in San Antonio. They were to march to the border, and if there were "good prospects of success," were to enter the enemy territory.

General Somervell organized his army from the recruits or the new soldiers at Concepción. Among those chosen were Asa Hill and his sons, Jeffrey and John. They marched to Laredo, only to find that the invading Mexican army had already left. The Texans camped about three miles below the city and ordered its citizens to furnish supplies. Then they went on down the Rio Grande to the town of Guerrero (Ga rá rō), commanding the mayor there to supply them with more food and with blankets.

General Somervell now decided not to invade Mexico, so he and a number of his men returned, stopping finally at Gonzales. About three hundred of the force believed that Somervell was afraid and had not been directed to return. They still wanted to punish the Mexicans for their recent invasions and to go into Mexico to prevent more raids later. They chose Colonel William S. Fisher as their commanding officer and selected seven company commanders. Asa Hill and his two sons were among this group of men.

In charge of a "navy" of six flatboats on the Rio Grande was "General" Thomas J. Green. He selected John and the boys with him as a part of his force to bring up supplies by water and to destroy enemy boats.

At Mier (Mē är´), the next town the Texans reached below Guerrero, they demanded four times the provisions needed to keep the enemy from knowing how small their numbers were. They made a prisoner of the alcalde, or mayor, of the town and withdrew to wait for city officials to assemble the supplies.

Two days after the withdrawal of Somervell, a Texas scout came back to camp and reported, "General Ampudia (Ăm pōō´ dyä) with seven hundred soldiers has just arrived, and he also has

artillery."

"We will attack anyhow," Fisher declared. "We said we would if they did not furnish us with supplies, and they haven't done it."

Cautiously the Texans moved into Mier at midnight. John and his friends were stationed on the top of a flat-roofed building, near where the enemy cannon were located.

"Your job will be to keep the enemy from firing those cannon," a Texas officer told them.

The boys, who were good marksmen with their rifles, succeeded so well at their task that not a Mexican reached the cannon. The enemy tried roping the guns from behind a nearby wall, but every time a hand showed with a rope it was shot. Indeed, it seemed as if the Texans were winning the battle, but presently a man appeared bearing a white flag of truce or temporary peace and a message from the enemy: "We have seventeen hundred soldiers in the city and expect eight hundred more in a short time." The note, signed by the Mexican commander, called on the Texans to surrender and promised them good treatment if they would.

Some of the Texans did not want to give up,

but their retreat to the Rio Grande was cut off by a body of Mexican troops, and Colonel Fisher was wounded. Since the odds against them were about six to one, they surrendered.

They were told to march out on the plaza or open square of the town to stack their arms. John went along with the others, but before he reached the plaza, he took his rifle by the barrel and broke the wooden part to pieces on a stone.

"Why did you do that?" his captors asked him.

"Because I promised my brother I would never let it fall into the hands of an enemy," he replied. "He gave it to me."

They told General Ampudia about John's action and about the success of the boys in preventing the firing of the cannon. General Ampudia sent for John, took him to his headquarters, and treated him well. Because he was grieved over the loss of his own son in battle, Ampudia admired the brave boy who had been captured. When John asked for permission to see his father and Jeff, the latter having been wounded, the kind-hearted general readily granted his request.

The Battle of Mier was fought on Christmas day. A week later, New Year's day, the Mexicans left with their prisoners for Matamoros (Mä tä mō´ros), another town farther down the

81

Rio Grande. John, now called Juan (Hwan), rode beside General Ampudia. Juan's father also had a horse to ride, but the wounded brother had been left behind in a hospital. Crowds turned out along the way to see the prisoners and to cheer the victors.

At Matamoros, Juan and the other boys were taken to the headquarters of General Ampudia and given food and clothing. A surprise was in store there for them. It was a message from Santa Anna, the President and Dictator of Mexico, who had heard of the victory. He sent this order: "All Texan prisoners captured at Mier are to be forwarded immediately, by the way of Monterrey, to the City of Mexico. The Texan leaders are to be sent in advance as hostages for the good behavior of the men."

This treatment was quite different from what the Texans were expecting, for they thought they would be set free on the promise not to take up arms against Mexico again. However, the order had to be obeyed. On January 12, 1843, the Texas officers started out on foot, heavily guarded. Twenty days later the other soldiers followed on the long dreary march.

With them went all the boys but Juan, whom General Ampudia kept in Matamoros. There, he was enrolled in school as Juan C. C. Hill de Ampudia. Whether the general actually pretended that Juan was his real son is not clear, but he might have deceived others about the matter. Ampudia was of Polish descent, and natives of Matamoros might have thought that Juan was his son.

But Juan was not allowed to stay long in Matamoros. In due time Santa Anna, who had heard of the brave boy who had been kept behind, wanted to see him. He sent a letter to General Ampudia ordering that Juan be sent at once to Mexico City by way of Tampico, "under safe escort."

Just what constituted a "safe escort" was not stated in the order, but there were many lawless

Santa Anna looked up at the boy and smiled.

people in Mexico during those times. General
Ampudia, not wanting to take any chances, sent
along a captain, a lieutenant, two orderlies, and
a dozen or more soldiers. Juan, dressed in new
clothes, was given a beautiful little horse and a
new saddle and bridle.

The order was that Juan be sent directly
to Santa Anna; but when the party reached
Mexico City, they learned the dictator was sick.
Juan was taken to the home of the Archbishop
of Mexico, across the street from the National
Palace, where Santa Anna lived.

Finally, when Juan was told that Santa
Anna was ready to see him, an orderly was sent
to go with him. The boy was scared as he entered the large room where the Mexican leader
was waiting. He knew that his father and Jeff
were prisoners, and that their fate rested in the
hands of the dictator. He had heard that the
man was cruel; and he was afraid that if he said
or did the wrong thing, the freedom or even the
lives of his loved ones might be in danger.

The raised platform on which Santa Anna
was sitting was bordered with rich draperies of
red and gold, and pictures of Mexico's great
men hung on the walls. Especially prominent
was a picture of President Washington, the sight
of which revived Juan's courage.

Santa Anna looked up at the boy and smiled.

Juan noticed that he was dressed in simple clothes, and he did not look like a bad man. In fact, Juan rather liked his appearance.

The Mexican President extended his hand to Juan as he greeted him. When the two were seated again, Santa Anna said, "Well, my young friend, I am glad to meet you. General Ampudia has said much about your character and your brave conduct at Mier."

Juan's face flushed. He hastened to say that he deserved no special credit for bravery, but before much else could be said, two men entered the room and were introduced to the boy. One of them was the Vice President of Mexico, and the other was the Secretary of War.

Soon it was made plain that they had been called in to consult with Santa Anna about Juan. The Mexican President wanted to adopt the boy as his own son and educate him in the National Military College at Chapultepec (Chä pōōl tä pĕk) Palace for a career in the army.

Juan stammered his thanks but let the three know that he would have to consult with his father before replying to the kind offer.

"Besides," he added, "I cannot serve in your army, for if a war should break out between this country and Texas, I would go home to serve there. I could never fight my own country."

Santa Anna smiled and turned to the other

men. "Our prisoner is dictating terms to me," he told them.

Turning once more to Juan, the President of Mexico said, "Perhaps we might find some other school for you to attend."

"And I promised my mother to take care of my father and brother," Juan added. "But they are both in your hands, and I do not even know what has become of them."

"We will see about them," promised the dictator uncertainly. "But first I want you to come to my palace and be a son to Doña Dolores de Tosta (Dōñ´ yä Dō lō´räs dā Tōs´tä) and myself, at once."

"When Father and Jeff reach Mexico City,

will you release them and let them go back home?"

When Santa Anna did not reply immediately to the question, Juan repeated it. At length the dictator answered, "Yes, when they come, if your father consents to your staying and getting an education, I will free both your father and brother and send them home."

Two weeks later Juan's father arrived. He enjoyed a happy reunion with his son. The dictator kept his promise. He returned Asa Hill to Matamoros, where Jeffrey, now recovered from his wound, joined him, and the two went home. Juan's mother missed her youngest born, but he visited her sometimes and wrote her often.

True to his promise, Santa Anna sent Juan

to one of the best schools in Mexico, the *Minería,* a school for mining engineers, where he graduated with honors. Later he studied medicine and became a practicing physician in the city of Puebla.

While Juan was going to school, he boarded in dormitories, but every Sunday he visited with Santa Anna and his wife, both of whom he learned to like very much.

The dictator did everything possible to help his adopted son, but Juan never forgot his own Texas home. He wrote regularly to his parents and always called himself a Texan. For many years he was a member of the Texas Veterans Association, an organization of men who had fought in the War of the Texas Revolution.

In 1855, he fell in love with a beautiful Mexican girl, the sister of a prominent Mexican painter. He used the occasion as an opportunity to visit his mother to win her consent to the marriage, which she promptly gave. Four children were born in the family. Juan died in Monterrey in 1904, but one of his daughters moved to Austin with two of her daughters, who were educated there.

Relatives and descendants of Juan were prominent later in Texas. One of them, George A. Hill, Jr., was Vice President of the Texas Historical Association, President of the Houston Oil

Company, and one of the founders of the San Jacinto Museum of History.

Juan followed with interest and sympathy the later careers of Santa Anna and Ampudia. The president's wife died before Juan had known her very long. Santa Anna lost his office and his power, being in and out of Mexico several times and sometimes in exile. Juan found it hard to believe all the stories he heard about the cruelty of the Mexican leader. Certainly Santa Anna was kind to him, and he in turn tried to be kind to others. It was reported that Juan rescued the younger brother of General Ampudia from prison and saved him from being shot.

War is an occupation which young boys sel-

dom follow, and Juan is not to be remembered so much for his fighting as for his other deeds. He went along "to take care of father and Jeff," and he did that task so well that he attracted the attention of his enemies. No doubt they mistreated some other Texans, but they were kind to Juan. Because he was brave and kept his word to his mother and brother, he became a hero, even in the eyes of his enemies.

— *J. A. Rickard*

Things to Do

1. Discuss the story with your classmates, using these questions:
   a. What happened to Juan in Matamoros?
   b. Why was he sent to Mexico City?
   c. Why did Santa Anna want to adopt Juan?
   d. What promise was made to Juan by the Mexican President?
   e. Why did Juan refuse to go to a military school?
   f. What happened to Juan in his later life?
2. There are several paragraphs in the story that tell you the kind of boy that Juan was. Here is one paragraph:

   They were told to march out to the plaza, or open square, of the town to stack their arms. John went along with the others; but before he reached the plaza, he took his rifle by the barrel and broke the wooden part to pieces on a stone.

   Find other paragraphs that help you to understand Juan.

Narciso, the Mexican Boy Hero

Some of the world's greatest heroes have been boys or girls. Almost every nation has one or more of these heroes, children who did not have to wait till they were grown before they had a chance to do brave deeds.

Mexico had such a young hero. His deed of bravery was in battle, which made him all the more interesting, for boys do not usually go to war.

This boy was named Narciso Mendoza (När cē´sō Mān dō´zä). More than a century ago he lived in the pueblo of Cuautla (Kwä ōōt´ lä), or Morelos, about seventy miles from Mexico City. His little, red-roofed, squatty gray home was set in the midst of a citrus and fig orchard at the edge of the town.

This half-Indian, half-Spanish boy helped his father gather fruit when it was ripe. Sometimes he went with his father to one of the town plazas, or market places, to sell the fruit. In the spring he worked in the corn patch with his father. When the corn was dry in the summer, he helped his mother grind it and make tortillas (tŏr tē´yäs) over charcoal fires. In the winter he went to a school taught by a kindly priest.

When Narciso was ten years old, he began to hear his parents and their friends talking about war and shaking their heads sadly.

The boy did not understand all that they said, but he did know that Spain was ruling his country. It seemed that the Mexicans did not like the Spanish rule; they wanted to be free from Spain, to have their own government. When Spain refused to let the Mexicans have their own government, they rebelled, and fighting began. The Mexicans raised an army and had their own leaders and rulers. Narciso knew one of these men, the good Morelos, for he had been in their humble home. Narciso's father was a soldier under Morelos.

In the second year of the war the fighting drew nearer to Narciso's home town. One day his father came home with a serious face. He told his wife and son that the enemy was marching on the town. They would barely have time to leave before the fighting began.

"We will stay here to defend our home," replied Narsico's mother, and there they stayed.

When the Royalist army, composed of both Spanish and Mexican troops, attacked Cuautla, all the people helped defend the town. Even little Narciso did his part. He did not carry a gun, but he carried water and food to the soldiers and ran errands for them.

The siege had been going on ten days when one morning the enemy made a fierce attack. For more than six hours the fighting raged back and forth across the plaza and in the streets nearby. Narciso, who had taken some tortillas to his father, could not even go back home. He remained beside his father.

Suddenly, the Mexican soldiers heard a cry, "They have taken the plaza! They have taken the plaza!"

Though it was proved afterwards that this was a false alarm, it caused the Mexican soldiers to lose courage. Up one of the streets they fled. So fast did they leave that they did not even take with them a large, loaded cannon that was in the middle of the street. It was ready to fire and was even pointed toward the enemy.

When the Royalist soldiers saw this cannon, they hurried forward to capture it. Everyone knew that they would then turn it on the Mexicans and kill many of them.

But the enemy soldiers never took the cannon, for as they came nearer, Narciso darted out from the Mexican lines. He was twenty feet away before his father saw him.

"Catch my boy! He will be killed!" shouted Narciso's father. A Mexican soldier ran after the boy and grabbed at him. He caught Narciso's coat sleeve for a moment, but the boy slipped out of the coat and kept running toward the cannon. During all this time, guns were firing, the bullets thick in the air around Narciso, but he did not stop a second.

Reaching the huge cannon just ahead of the Royalist soldiers, he touched a match to the place where it was fired, as he had seen his father do.

There was a loud roar as the cannon spouted flame. A large hole was torn in the enemy ranks, and their troops fell back in alarm. The Mexicans now rushed forward and drove them away.

Through the bravery of the boy the patriot army was saved. Later the patriots escaped

There was a loud roar

from the city. Several years afterward the Mexicans won their freedom — and Narciso had helped them win it.

-- *J. A. Rickard*

Things to Do

1. Members of the class may find the following parts of the story to read them aloud:
   a. Where Narciso lived and what kinds of work he did.
   b. Why the Mexicans did not like to be ruled by the Spanish.
   c. How the battle near Narciso's home began.
   d. Why the big cannon was left in the middle the street.
   e. How Narciso saved the patriot army.

Adventure on the Frontier

The Defense of Big Sandy

The feel of the first frost was still in the air
when Billy and his mother returned to their
three-room, unpainted farm home, on the edge
of the woods near the big field. Billy was panting as he trudged barefoot into the yard.

"Whew! but it's a job to water fifty head of
cattle from a bucket well! I'm glad it's over for
the day."

His mother did not answer, and when he
saw her looking intently toward the big pasture
west of the house, he looked too. He saw strange
cattle coming and more following them. The

woods seemed alive with them and every steer was bawling.

Before the boy could ask what it meant, he noticed two riders making their way along the narrow footpath that led to the yard gate. One of them, a straight-backed fellow who filled every inch of his saddle, took off his huge gray hat and spoke.

"Good morning, ma'am. Is your husband at home?"

"No, sir, he is not here right now."

"Is anybody at home over yonder?" he asked next, pointing north toward the Hasty place, which was also on the edge of the woods near the big field.

"No, they are gone too."

"And there's nobody at the Hudson place either," blurted out Billy, pointing toward another house. "All Big Sandy's gone off to pick cotton."

Billy's mother caught his eye then, and he realized that he had told those strangers something that she did not want them to know. She was the kind of person who could just look at one and make him know what she was thinking. She was slim, and straight, and pretty, even when she was not dressed up. When a stranger tried to guess her age, he almost always said twenty instead of thirty-five. This morning she was wearing a clean cotton dress, and the wind was blowing her brown hair just enough to make it look ruffled. He could tell that she was worried; but she did not show her feelings to those men. She faced them squarely.

The man who had spoken to her must have been worried too, for he kept shifting from one stirrup to the other and pulling at the rim of his big gray hat. Finally he said, "Well, ma'am, I'm Jack Harper, foreman of the Bar Z Ranch, and we've leased Big Sandy for grazing."

Billy saw his mother catch her breath as she answered, "You can't turn your stock in here. We have this land rented, and it's ours till January 1. We have our own stock in the fields."

"But J. Y. Pullam owns Big Sandy, ma'am, and he leased it to us yesterday. He said you didn't have any crops that the cattle could bother."

"No, the rain came too late to save our corn and cotton, but there is crab grass in the fields, and our own cattle and horses are grazing it."

"You can turn your stock in the pasture," he said, motioning towards the woods and the strange cows. "I see it's fenced off from the fields."

"There's no grass in that pasture. Our cattle would starve there."

"My men will help you, ma'am. They'll drive all your stock out and keep them separated from ours."

Billy could tell that his mother was trying hard to keep her voice calm as she replied, "No, thank you, and don't you drive a cow inside that fence. And I might remind you that it's unlawful to cut barbed wire fences in Texas."

Harper stiffened in his saddle and picked up the reins from his horse's neck. "Well, I'm sorry the men folks are gone, and I had rather not have trouble. But we leased that field and paid for it, and I'll give you half an hour to get your livestock out of it."

"And we'll give you that same time to get your cattle out of our pasture."

With that she went in the house. Billy followed her. She shut the door, but he peeped through the window and saw the two men still sitting uncertainly on their horses.

"The Bar Z! Whew!" Billy whistled under his breath. "If what Dad says about them is halfway true, they're a bunch of rustlers, crooks, and robbers all rolled into one. And the Bar Z owner — he — he killed a man in Cleburne last year."

Billy's mother no longer pretended to be calm. Her face had a strained and hunted look. "Yes, and those cattle will strip our fields bare and eat all the grass that has grown since the July rains. And they'll tear down our fences, and our own cattle will stray off and be stolen by

that bunch of thieves."

Billy was beginning to feel scared himself, and such a big lump rose in his throat that he could not answer. His mother went on, "Oh, if only Daddy, or your older brother, or some of the other men were here! But it's that bunch of ruffians against a woman and a boy!"

Billy thought he had better act brave, whether he felt that way or not. He replied, "But we've got Ring and Nero, Mom, to help. And those men are half scared already. They're still talking things over. See?"

To prove what he was saying, he pointed through the window; but even as he spoke, the two men rode slowly back through the woods. His mother straightened and patted him on the back.

"Bless you, my son, we'll fight 'em — you and I and the dogs. But I'm not sure what they'll do."

"All the gates are nailed up except the one in front of the Hudson place, in the middle of that lane running down to the Brazos River."

"That's where they'll try to get in," she decided, "and that's where we'll have to take our stand."

"You mean with the gun, Mom?" asked Billy as he eyed the long-barreled, twelve-gauge shotgun hanging in a rack on the wall.

"I don't know," she hesitated; then she added, "No, I guess not."

"But we'd better get to that gate pretty soon, hadn't we?" asked Billy as he looked through the window again. "The cows are already headed toward that lane."

All of a sudden, it seemed, his mother made up her mind what to do. She reached to a nail on the wall and took from it a five-foot trace chain with a lock on the end.

"Take this to the Hudson gate. Wrap it twice around the gate and the fence post, about the middle," she told him. "I'll come on in a minute. Stay till I get there. And run!"

As Billy grabbed the chain and started out through the back door, she added, "Go down the back trail from the barn. Take Ring and Nero with you!"

Billy went by the barn and loosed the two big shepherd dogs, who went bounding ahead of him as he ran down the trail. It took him only a minute to lock the gate, but he was none too soon, for a few cows had already entered the eighty-foot-wide lane, and more were slowly coming out of the woods. His eyes followed the lane until it broadened out along the upper banks of the Brazos River three hundred yards away, and stopped at the edge of the water.

Billy guessed that, when the men found the

gate locked, they might fill the lane so full of
cattle that the fence would cave in. Then they
would not be violating the law in the same way
as if they cut the wires. Once the cows were inside, he and his mother would be helpless, for
their own stock would be lost among them.
His eyes blurred at the thought. He stamped
his heel on the ground and wished that his mother
would hurry.

He did not have much time to work out the
problem, for two riders were already moving
down the lane toward the river. He could hear
the rising rumble of bawling cattle drifting in
behind them. Presently, the men reached the
end of the lane next to the river, where they
turned around and headed their horses back
toward the rushing cattle. Some of the animals
nearest the riders stopped and turned about uncertainly. Far up at the other end of the lane

Billy could see the cattle coming in, urged along by three other riders, one of whom was Harper. Oh, why didn't his mother hurry?

Then he saw her coming. At first he could not tell what she had in her hands, but as she moved closer he saw two pitchforks, his own little one with its pecan sapling handle and his daddy's larger one.

He hurried to meet her. Between breaths she told him what to do.

"Guard the fence south of the gate," she gasped. "Punch cattle that get against the wires. I'll watch from here back to the woods."

"Yes, ma'am," answered Billy. "And may I take the dogs with me?"

"Take Nero; I'll take Ring. Let him bark

all he wants to — the more the better."

The big brown dogs wanted to — that was plain. In fact, they were already running up and down the fence barking as loudly as they could. Their bristles were not up, for they were not angry. Indeed, they were enjoying themselves very much. Billy had taught them to chase cows; this was going to be a great day.

The lane was milling with cows; more were coming from the woods. Billy guessed there might be a thousand of them, if he could have counted them. His mother gave him some more instructions before he started.

"Go up and down the fence. Keep the cattle from pushing it in," she told him. "Don't stick them with your pitchfork, just punch them hard enough to make them get back from the wires. Now, hurry!"

Billy fairly flew. He could see the two men on horseback at the river end of the lane and the three other horsemen at the north end of it. More cattle were coming into the lane, but not any were allowed to leave it. They were being crowded up more and more between the two fences. The one on the west side would hold, Billy felt sure, for it was made of new cedar posts and had four strands of new wire. But the one on his side was not so good. It would not hold long.

Just as he reached the gate, a large steer poked his head through the wires. Billy set the dog on him, and Old Nero barked so loudly that the animal backed away in a hurry. A second steer was crowded up against another part of the fence. Billy punched him hard enough to make him move back, but another took his place, and still another. Presently the boy was running up and down the fence punching and hitting cattle with all his might.

By this time the lane was so full that Billy did not see how another steer could possibly be crowded in. The posts were close together, and for that he was thankful. But the cattle could break the wire any time. He didn't see how either the posts or the wire could hold out much longer. The dust was so thick, and the noise of bawling beef was so loud, that he could barely hear the dog bark. He wondered what his mother was doing.

Then he looked up and saw her coming. Her face was grimy, her dress was torn, and she was almost frantic. He could not tell what she was saying until she was close, but she was pointing toward the river.

"Go down there!" she yelled. "Take both dogs! I'll watch the fence here!"

Billy took a last poke at a steer. He saw one of the riders jump off his horse and crawl

through the fence. Straight toward the boy and
the dogs he came, with a long whip in his hand.
Billy felt like running, but he stood his ground.
He whistled to the dogs, all the while pointing
toward the man. Their bristles up, they started
toward him. Billy knew they would attack if
the man took one more step. He stood there a
full minute, watching the dogs, then turned and
slowly went back to his horse in the lane.

Billy looked around and saw his mother near
him. At the same time he heard a loud whistle.
It was coming from Jack Harper at the north end
of the lane. He was waving to the men on the
river side. He was no longer herding the cows
into the lane; in fact, they were moving out of
it. Slowly but surely the place was emptying
itself of its bawling herd.

Ten minutes later a horseman approached, took off his hat, and bowed. It was Harper.

"I know when I'm licked," he said. "And I don't like the idea of fighting women and children. Good day!"

He replaced his hat, wheeled his horse, and herded the last roving cow out of the lane.

Billy looked at his mother then, for she had sat down on the ground and was sobbing. He went to her and put his hand on her shoulder.

"Quit crying, Mom," he said gently. "It's time to laugh. We whipped 'em — a woman, two dogs, and a boy."

She dried her tears and stood up. Slowly, thoughtfully, she spoke, "Son, sometimes people cry when they are glad. But you were a man today. Yes, we whipped them — a woman, two dogs, and a real man."

— *J. A. Rickard*

Things to Do

1. Discuss the meanings of the following expressions with your classmates:
   a. Leased Big Sandy for grazing.
   b. It's unlawful to cut barbed wire fences in Texas.
   c. Will strip our fields bare.
   d. It's a bunch of ruffians against a woman and a boy.
2. Billy was afraid in the story. What did he do about his fear? Do you think that what he did helped him to develop courage?
3. Do you think that the title of the story is a good one? Why?
4. The story could have had a different ending. Discuss other endings for the story.

Rustlers in the Canyon

The May sun said it was noon when Floyd Mason and Joe Donovan dismounted on a high knoll overlooking Devil's Canyon. For a full minute they gazed at the wild natural scene below them; then Joe spoke.

"So that's where the lost herd is — we hope."

"It's got to be there," said Floyd almost fiercely. "Those cows can't be any other place on the whole range. If we don't find them, I won't go off to school this fall. And Dad won't be able to pay that note on the land he bought, and he may lose it, and —"

"Now, now, Floyd," interrupted his friend. "Don't borrow trouble. Maybe they are there, and we'll find them. But they'll have to be near the upper end of that canyon, where the trees are not so thick."

"And if they are," echoed Floyd, "It's a mystery to me how they got there."

Joe made no answer, but it was quite evident that it was a mystery. The canyon was somewhat in the form of a bottle, its mouth lying east and downhill enough to drain. The western end, half a mile wide at its broadest part, seemed to nestle up to the banks below the Cap Rock, which itself looked like a low-lying chain of mountains, flat on top.

As far as the two could see, the walls were steep everywhere except at the lower end. The whole inside of the canyon was filled with brush and trees that grew thicker toward the mouth. Floyd guessed that it was a quarter of a mile wide and five miles long.

"There seems to be no opening except from below," said Joe, "but I thought I saw some cows in the upper end."

"The only thing to do is to find or make a

way up from the mouth," said Floyd, as he mounted and headed his horse back down the hill.

At the lower end they found the bed of a half-dry stream and decided to try going up it. Fifty yards of travel led them to a dry waterfall ten feet high. Dismounting to lead their horses up a worn trail to the left, they soon found their path blocked by heavy underbrush. Floyd was glad then that he had brought his hand axe, for Joe did not have one. He went to work, cutting away limbs to open up a trail wide enough for themselves and the horses.

So absorbed did they become in working their way up the canyon that they forgot all about lunch till Floyd happened to look at the sun. Already it was riding its downward path in the sky.

"Whew!" muttered the boy. "Here it is two o'clock, and we haven't had anything to eat."

"Maybe we'd better have lunch and let our horses graze," said Joe, stopping to dismount. "Here's a break in the brush and some grass."

They removed their saddles to allow the sweaty backs of the horses to dry, and Floyd used his saddle as a lean-to while he ate his lunch of cold biscuits and barbecued beef. A pool of water in a nearby gully was muddy, but it was wet, as Floyd remarked. Joe thought it a good sign, even if they could not find any cow tracks near.

"We're not more than a mile up the canyon, though," guessed the man. "We'll have to hurry if we finish riding out the place before dark."

As soon as they had swallowed their last bites they saddled up and, leading their horses, started up the canyon. Floyd had to use his axe frequently on limbs that barred their path.

During the second and third miles there were not so many limbs, and the brush was thinner. There were plain signs of cattle too, they saw with growing excitement: they came across a trail freshly marked with cow tracks and bits of red hair on a bush.

Floyd forgot all about the time until he saw his partner look at his watch and announce, "Another hour till sundown."

At that moment they heard a distinct bawl. It was less than a mile away, and there was an answering calf bleat.

"Old Mother Cow is calling her baby, and it is answering," said Joe, leaning forward and lifting his horse's reins to quicken his steps.

"They're both calling us," said Floyd, pressing his horse with his heels to keep up.

More undergrowth barred their way. Floyd fretted as he hacked away at it nervously. When the trees finally grew thinner, they remounted and made greater speed. They could hear the cattle plainly.

At last they sighted them. The animals were grazing, or lying down and chewing their cuds, in an open space about a hundred yards across. Joe, in the lead, stopped abruptly. He dismounted, motioned to Floyd to dismount also, then put two fingers over his mouth to indicate silence.

"There's somebody — up there," he half whispered, pointing up the canyon.

Floyd looked and saw three saddled horses eating grass at the west end of the clearing. One of them snorted. Farther on, half hidden by bushes, they could see the smoke of a camp fire rising lazily. Two men were at the fire. Presently a third man joined them.

"Rustlers,"' said Joe. "They're watching this herd, probably expecting to drive it off soon."

"I know one of them," said Floyd. "Tim Murphy. He used to work for us. At least, that's his horse."

"You stay here," said Joe, putting his horse's reins in the boy's hands. "Take the horses back down the trail, out of sight."

"What are you going to do?"

"Slip up this canyon for a closer look. Maybe learn what they're up to."

The tall man bent over till his body was close to the ground and disappeared up the canyon. Floyd, slowly leading the horses back into heavier brush, wondered how his friend would fare. He could see that the bushy gully up which Joe was creeping ran within a few feet of the three men. If he was quiet enough, he could crawl close to the men, but if they should

see him — Floyd shuddered to wonder what he would do then. It seemed a long time before Joe returned, although it could not have been over fifteen minutes. The man's face was grim, as he took the reins of his horse.

"I know every one of them," he said. "We must hurry back to the ranch as soon as we can."

"You mean tonight? It must be close to sundown now."

"I know it. But they are planning to leave here with that herd tomorrow afternoon. If we don't go back with the news at once, it'll be too late to head them off. We must find our way out of this canyon before dark or have trouble."

Floyd fell in behind his companion· on the trail. Going back was easier than coming up had been, but so great was Joe's haste that he rode his horse too near a deep ravine near the mouth of the gully. The animal stumbled and fell, throwing Joe to the bed of the ravine, ten feet below. As he landed with a sickening thud, the anxious boy heard a groan.

Floyd jumped down the bank of the ravine. Joe had managed to raise up on one elbow.

"Don't move me - - yet," he said. "I think - - a leg's broken."

It was; halfway between ankle and knee. Joe was the calmer of the two.

"We'll have to put it in a splint," he said. "Cut three cedar sticks, half as big around as your wrist and about a foot long. There are some — on the side of the bank."

Floyd took his hand axe and, to keep down a growing panic, worked hard. In ten minutes the sticks were ready. Joe showed him how to flatten them on one side and notch the ends.

"Now cut the leather strings off my saddle," directed the man. The boy worked fast, but it was almost dark before he finished putting the splint on the leg. To climb back on his horse, the crippled man straddled Floyd's neck. The boy staggered under the load, but once Joe had hold of the saddle horn he pulled himself up.

"Now, let's hurry out of here," he said, "to find our way home."

Soon they were out of the canyon. They tried to follow the trail back as they had come, but with the moon not yet up, it was a hopeless task. Before long they had returned to the canyon.

"We're lost," said Joe. "We'll have to give rein to our horses. Maybe they'll go home of their own accord."

The two started out again, with Floyd in the lead. Before they had gone a hundred yards he heard a noise, and looked back to see Joe sway in the saddle. He jumped down and hurried back, barely reaching the man in time to keep him from falling off.

"I almost passed out," admitted Joe. "I'm afraid I'll have to lie down. That leg is beginning to act up."

The moon had risen by this time. Floyd filled his hat with water from a nearby hole and bathed his friend's face, as he lay on the ground.

"You go on, Floyd, and leave me here. I'll be safe."

"I can't do that. If something happened to you, I'd never forgive myself."

"Nothing will happen to me. I don't be-

lieve I can ride that jolty horse any farther."

They rested awhile, Floyd trying to persuade his friend to mount again. But every move brought a groan of pain. They gave up trying. Floyd made his coat into a pillow for Joe's head, and threw the man's saddle blanket over him. He watered the horse and tied him to a bush, then filled Joe's hat with water and set it by him. The last thing, he adjusted the splint to make Joe more comfortable.

"I'll be back early in the morning," he promised. "Lie still, and try to sleep."

Floyd knew his home lay to the north. Thanks to his mother, he could locate the North Star, which was shining brightly. The trail grew long though. Twice he had to stop to hunt for a way around ravines. Once he had to cut through with his axe. He grew so sleepy that he dismounted and walked awhile to keep awake.

He wondered how much farther it was. He had to take the news to his father about that herd, and he had to return to Joe. What if the man should become delirious, as wounded people sometimes do? His father and the rest of them might go after the cattle, but he was going back after Joe.

He wondered why daylight was so long in coming. He was tired of trying to keep his eyes on the North Star and on the ground at the same time. He was tired in body too. He grew sleepy again and almost fell off his horse.

Daylight found him a mile from home. He gave a glad shout as he saw the smoke rising from the kitchen chimney. Pressing his heels against his horse's sides, he galloped into the yard.

His story was soon told. While he ate breakfast, his father and five men started for the canyon. Another cowboy went with Floyd to rescue Joe. With their aid the crippled man managed to stay on his horse.

"We'll have a doctor the first thing," promised Floyd.

"Oh, I'm all right," said Joe, "but I would have been in real trouble if it hadn't been for you. You took care of me like a veteran."

"Guess we'll have to initiate him into the mystic order of cowboys," said the man with Floyd. "Especially if they capture the rustlers and drive in the herd."

They did both. By nightfall the doctor had set Joe's leg and he was feeling much better. Floyd was happy. He had learned that neither size nor age was important. Finding a hard job and doing it — that was what counted — on the range and all through life.

— *J. A. Rickard*

Things to Do

1. Make a television show of this story and give it to another fifth grade or to a group of younger children. Here are the scenes in the story:
   a. Floyd and Joe go into the canyon.
   b. Spying the rustlers.
   c. Returning to the ranch to warn the owner of the cattle.
   d. Joe falls into the canyon.
   e. They lose their way home.

f. Floyd can take Joe no further and leaves him in the canyon.

g. Floyd finds his way to his father's ranch.

h. The rescue of Joe and the herd.

2. Here are several things that you and your classmates will need to do:

a. Illustrate each scene in the story.

b. Write the dialogue for each scene and decide what sound effects could be used. If your school owns a tape recorder, put the dialogue on tape.

c. Make the screen for your TV set from a box and put your scenes on a roll of paper that can be turned for each scene.

d. Put the recordings and your scenes together for a real TV show.

3. Cowboy songs or ballads could be used as a part of the show. Use your imagination to make the show a fine one!

Prairie Fire

The August wind was blowing so hard that Sam Miller could hardly open the front door at Bar G headquarters. His father, in the yard, was shaking his head as the boy approached.

"The whole range is a powder box," he said. "One match would start such a fire as no one around here ever saw before."

Sam understood his father's thoughts all too well. If their pastures burned now, their cattle would not have enough winter grazing and would have to be sold at a loss. His own little herd would be lost too, and he would not have enough money to buy the things he had planned —a new saddle for Smoky and a watch, maybe. They could not make the fall payment on their land and might lose it. Some of their livestock would burn; even the house and barns might catch fire.

"I've been worried," Sam replied, "but what can we do?"

"High Pockets and I will start plowing. If we can break a ten-foot strip around the home pasture, maybe a fire will not leap over it. Can you and Smoky go to the store?"

"Yes, sir. What shall we get?"

"Tow sacks, or house brooms. Whatever you can buy. If nothing can be bought we will gather broom weed."

"All right, sir," Sam replied, taking a five-dollar bill from his father's hand. Thirty minutes later he was riding up to the store five miles away.

The bald-headed merchant, whose store was the only one in town, welcomed the boy, but he was out of tow sacks and could spare only six brooms.

"I'm having other calls for them," he explained. "I hope you don't have to use them."

"I hope so too," answered Sam. At once he and Smoky were on their way back.

He was about halfway home when he saw in the southeast a long line of light-colored smoke hugging the ground. Then he caught the smell of burned grass and saw pieces of blackened ashes in the air. He pressed his heels against Smoky's sides; the animal broke into a gallop.

His mother was waiting in the front yard. "Dad and High Pockets have already gone to the fire," she said hurriedly. "I'm to take the brooms. You're to haul water in the cart."

She mounted her big sorrel and Sam handed her the bundle of brooms. Off she went at a gallop.

Quickly Sam hitched Smoky between the shafts of the cart, a homemade affair, with a platform between two wheels. On it was fastened a large oaken barrel, with a board seat between the barrel and the shafts. A double thickness of heavy canvas lay over the top of the barrel, held on by a steel hoop that could be pushed down tightly around the outside.

Sam filled the barrel, using a three-gallon zinc bucket to dip water from the tank behind the barns. As soon as the boy gave the word,

Smoky was off at a fast trot. They went bump-
ing across the pasture toward the fire, a good
five miles away.

Nat Miller met him a quarter of a mile from
the blaze. He and three other grim-faced men
lifted the cart, barrel and all, and poured the
water into a larger barrel nearby.

"Keep it up, Son," he said. "We need all
the water you can haul, as fast as you can haul
it."

"I will, Dad. Do you think we can stop the
fire?"

"We hope to. We've put out a mile of it already, but it's doing much damage. Already it has burned six sections bare."

"Where did it start?"

"At the highway, in a Lazy S pasture. Probably some camper, or someone careless with a cigarette."

Groups of fire fighters began to come up to wet their mops and brooms to which they had tied rags. One cowboy had tied his shirt around a long stick. None of them lingered. Each dipped his equipment in water to hurry back for more fighting. Sam caught the spirit and rushed all the more.

On his second trip, the men who met him were confident. "We'll lick the fire if the wind doesn't change," they told him.

It was dark before he delivered the third barrel, but he had no trouble seeing the way: the light from the fire showed him. Only two tired and dirty men were present. Sam knew without being told that the wind had changed, and the fire had taken on new life.

"Your dad was too busy to come," one of them said, as he dipped up water in his hat, drank, and splashed some on his shirt mop. "But he said to tell you to keep fighting."

"I surely will," promised Sam.

The moon rose, but smoke and cinders dulled

its glow. Sam and Smoky kept steadily at their task until the boy felt too tired to move. All night long they hauled water, while the fire crept closer and closer to their pasture. At times it seemed almost out—only to blaze again in some other place. He was afraid the strip of plowed ground was too narrow to stop it. His dad and High Pockets had not had time to make it more than six feet wide. A strong wind might blow cinders across.

Sam's father met him at the plowed land just at daylight. Never before had the boy seen

his dad so tired and worried.

"We have the fire headed off on the sides," he said, "but it is still coming this way. The only hope of saving our pasture is to do some back-firing. I need you to help me."

Forgetting how tired he was, Sam sprang from his cart seat. "Yes, sir," he said. "What can I do?"

"We must burn a strip south of the plowed ground. I'll start the fire and spread it. You take this wet broom, watch the north side, and put out any blaze that jumps across."

Nat twisted dry grass around a long stick, set fire to it, and began walking slowly through the grass as he held the torch to the ground. Sam stamped out two small blazes, but a larger one flamed almost beyond control. Nat had to help him put it out.

Slowly the two worked their way westward. Gradually the fires that Nat had started widened the space between the rushing blaze and their pasture.

Sam could see the main fire plainly when the smoke lifted. Men were running back and forth and shouting; now and then he could catch some of their words. He wondered, with a sinking feeling, if their burned strip would extend far enough west by the time the main blaze reached them. He was afraid it would not.

Nat must have decided the same thing, for he called out, "Make a torch like mine! Run on two hundred yards ahead and begin firing. We must burn out this strip before the main fire reaches us."

Sam hurriedly obeyed, dragging his lighted broom through the grass as fast as he could to make it catch. A thin line of smoke sprang up behind him, but the big fire was closer now, and there were another hundred yards to go. The heat was almost more than the boy could stand as it clawed his hands and leaped at his face. But he kept on. With one last spurt he dragged his torch over the soil. He reached the end of the plowed ground where he turned about to keep the fire from spreading farther west. Since he had no broom, he stamped on it with his shoes. Nat came to his aid, the two finishing the job. Then, their own fire quenched, silently they watched the larger blaze draw nearer.

They saw it rush to meet the feeble backfire and die out as the two blazes joined. In thirty minutes only scattered pieces of smoking brush or grass remained. Dozens of cowboy firefighters were present by this time, and they were beginning to relax and joke with each other.

Sam found Smoky grazing a hundred yards from the smoke. Some of the water in the barrel he was pulling had spilled, but there was enough left for a drink all 'round. A number of cattle had died; fifty sections of land had burned bare of grass, but the cowmen refused to be sad. Even High Pockets was happy.

"Shouldn't be surprised if it rains tonight," High Pockets said, eyeing the sky.

It did rain. Sam awakened to the sound of thunder and the patter of drops on the roof. He said a little prayer of thankfulness: their cattle had been saved and would have grass to eat. Though some of the ranchmen had lost heavily, more grass would grow before winter. For all these he uttered his thanks, adding a few more for Mother and Dad.

— J. A. Rickard

Things to Do

1. Why were prairie fires destructive and dangerous?
2. How were house brooms and tow sacks used to fight prairie fires?
3. How did Sam's father use a plow to prevent the spread of the fire?
4. How did "backfiring" help stop the blaze?
5. Why did Sam feel thankful?
6. Write a short description of how early ranchers fought prairie fires. Compare your description with modern methods of controlling and fighting fires.

Chasing Mustangs on Texas Plains

The mustang is well known in the southwest. He descended from the horses that the Spanish brought to Mexico. Before many years passed, there were many mustangs, and they had spread into regions north of Mexico. In time, they became small, tough, hardy, wild animals of the prairie. In this story, a pioneer cowboy, who later was one of the founders of the city of Lubbock, tells about chasing wild mustangs on a Texas prairie.

In the summer of 1880 a man from Coleman County started to New Mexico with some sixty or seventy cow ponies to sell to cattlemen of that state.

When they were about twenty miles west of where the city of Lubbock is now located, they ran into a bunch of wild mustangs. Their horses became mixed up with them, and *all* of them stampeded. When the chase was over, the owner had left only some eight or ten gentle old horses; all the rest had quit him.

Three summers later, Sam S. Gholson asked me to go with him and try to locate and capture the horses which were lost by the Coleman County man in the stampede. Mr. Gholson was acquainted with this man, and he had told him

that he could have all of them he could capture.
Gholson and I started out with two good horses
apiece. We knew the brand to look for on the
lost horses, and we also knew that none of the
mustangs were branded.

At that time large herds of untamed mustangs roamed the Plains. We had a pair of good
field glasses with which we could read a brand
as far as three miles when the weather was clear.
We spent two days riding over Lubbock and
Hockley Counties; our trip was made interesting
by seeing herds of wild horses. It was difficult,

though, to get near enough to them to use our field glasses. I have noticed that a horse can see a man a distance of three miles or farther, but a cow cannot see more than about a mile.

As we were getting short on grub, we pulled out for Estacado to re-stock our provisions, which consisted, for the most part of bacon, crackers, and coffee. At Estacado we told some good old Quaker people our mission. One of the Hunt boys (I think it was Lint Hunt, brother of Dr. J. W. Hunt, former President of McMurry College at Abilene), told us that thirty or forty mustangs were grazing west of Estacado about eight or ten miles, and some of them were branded.

We felt sure that the herd included at least some of the horses for which we were searching. We camped for the night some three miles west of the town, and started out early the next morning looking for those horses. As Gholson had the field glasses, he was the first one to see them. He told me that they were the horses all right, but that only about half of them were branded.

We decided that I was to give them the first chase while Gholson made camp. We knew that they would not leave their accustomed range, so I just kept near enough to them to keep them running at full speed, while most of the time my horse was going at a slow gallop. This was possible because the mustangs ran in a circle and would not leave the location where they were found. I was on the inside of that circle.

After I had chased them about an hour, Gholson came up and continued the chase. I went back to the camp for a rest. The mustangs followed a four- or five-mile circle from the lake where they watered. The moon was shining brightly, so we kept up the chase two nights and part of three days. We kept them moving all the time, never allowing them to stop for sleep or a drink.

All bands of mustangs have a boss or a leader, usually a stallion. In this herd of horses the leader was a beautiful, unbranded, blood bay stallion. He was the gamest animal I ever saw, and most of the time he was in the lead. When one of the band would lag or drop behind, however, the boss horse would leave his position at the lead and return and drive it back into the ranks. At times he would bite or turn his heels on one that was lagging.

He did not give up, even after we had worried them down enough to drive them any direction we wanted them to go. Even then he would drop back and make a dash for one of the riders. Several times he came to within ten feet of us, and we saw that we were going to have to do something about it. We shot him,

and after that we had no more trouble with the
other horses.

We drove them to branding pens which were
located on the ground where the main business
street of Post City is now located. After putting
them in corrals for the night, we went to the
Llano Ranch headquarters, about two and a half
miles to the southwest, and stayed all night.

We had captured thirty-six horses, and our
next task was to shoe them. We roped and hog-
tied every one of them, one at a time, and put

on the shoes. We put them on in such a way that when the horse took a step the shoe barely passed over the thin portion of the leg and stopped at the joint above the hoof. We simply mashed the ends of each shoe almost together and put them on the legs, not on the hoofs. When he walked along peacefully, he could travel very well; but if he started to run, those shoes would bother him.

For about six weeks we kept them in a herd by day and locked them up in a corral at night. Eventually, we shipped them to Louisiana and sold them to cotton growers for a nice profit; but we earned it!

— Roley C. Burns, as told to J. A. Rickard

Things to Do

1. How did the herd of tame horses become lost?
2. What trick did Gholson and Burns use to recapture them?
3. What did the horse leader do to keep his followers faithful?
4. How did the captors prevent the captured horses from running off?
5. Make a list of all the facts that you learned about mustangs from this story.
6. Find other information about these wild ponies from books in your library.

The Fruit Tree Peddler

The calendar on the wall showed that it was August 15, 1886. United States Marshal Doc Frazier looked up from his desk and shook his head.

"It's not that you couldn't fill a deputy marshal's shoes, McDonald," he said. "Your reputation as a law man is good. But I have no salary to pay you, and you can't do this job by yourself."

McDonald leaned over the desk, his lean face tightening. "The cattlemen of this area want the Cherokee Strip cleaned out. Rustlers are stealing their stock and taking them out of the state. As a Ranger I can't follow them, but as a deputy marshal I can. As for the pay—they'll take care of that."

"I know it's bad," Frazier admitted, twisting in his chair. "Thieves, robbers, and murderers live in the Strip. There's little law enforcement there. It's a dull month when an M. K. & T. or a Santa Fe train is not robbed, a bunch of cattle lost, or a mail car shot full of holes."

"Then why do you hesitate?" McDonald asked patiently. "Just give me the badge of a United States marshal, and I'll take care of the details."

By way of reply Frazier took from his desk a badge and handed it to the visitor.

"All right—you win," he said with the air of a man who knew better. "You can do it if anybody can, but it's not a job for one man. The commission'll be drawn up in a day or two."

"I'll not wait," McDonald replied as he pocketed the badge. "But I'll not use this for awhile."

"May I inquire what your first move will be?"

"Before I can clean up the Strip, I'll have to know who the criminals are. I'll have to investigate thoroughly but in such a way as to avoid suspicion."

"You're on the right track," Frazier nodded in hearty agreement. "It would do no good to arrest some men whose only offense was that they have squatted on land to which they have no title. You need to find the leaders and enough evidence to convict them in court."

"Correct," agreed McDonald. "And as of today I'm turning detective."

He bought a paint pony and an old tenderfoot saddle, such as no plainsman would be caught using, and entered the Strip. Under his arm was a large book showing beautiful pictures of fruit trees—the kind of book that fruit tree peddlers carried.

Carefully avoiding the appearance of being an officer, or a cowman, or even a Texan, he concealed his badge in his vest pocket. The stirrups an inch too long for his legs, he sat on his horse uncertainly, as if he were not used to riding. At times his steel-gray eyes stared vacantly; on the slightest occasion his lean face broke into a friendly grin. He appeared to be an inoffensive, easy-going, talkative peddler who was happy to

sit all day, whittling and swapping yarns with anybody.

After crossing the Red River and moving into the Strip, he had pleasant riding. No fruit tree peddler had ever dared to venture into that dangerous country, where men were robbed or murdered at the drop of a hat. He was not expecting much in the way of orders, but he was mistaken. The outlaws, almost to a man, looked at the beautifully colored pictures of delicious fruits, and their mouths watered. They saw visions of such trees growing by the doors of their dugouts or sod houses. Eagerly they fingered the wonderful pictures of pears, peaches, plums, and apples.

No money was to be paid until delivery, the friendly stranger told them, so they gave generous orders. All the while they were talking. The sympathetic, kindly natured peddler encouraged them to talk. He even admitted indirectly that he himself had been in a few hold-ups and other shady enterprises. Sometimes he grew angry and abused laws in general and law men in particular, and he usually wound up his long violent speeches by declaring that the farther away from both he could be, the better it suited him.

Under such gentle encouragement, would-be customers not only signed orders for fruit trees, but they told about the parts they had played in train robberies, cattle thefts, and murders. The slim, mild-looking tree man criticized the law, and matched their confessions with tales of bigger law violations in which he had engaged. Then, warmly shaking the rough hands of his newly found friends, he asked the path to the next house, mounted his old paint horse, and rode slowly away.

In every instance he promised "spring delivery." When he ended his trip at Guthrie, then a growing station on the Santa Fe, he knew exactly who had robbed trains, stolen cattle or horses, or committed other crimes. He had enough information to execute warrants for arrests. Also, he had orders for twenty-five hundred dollars worth of fruit trees for "spring delivery."

He began by swearing out warrants for the arrest of eight men located in one of the communities near Guthrie. But his worst jolt was yet to come. The Guthrie deputy looked at him with mild curiosity when he presented them and shook his head.

"Nothing doing," he said firmly. "You don't know that crowd. I do. It would take a company of soldiers to make those arrests; then some of the soldiers would be killed and some of the outlaws would get away. No ten men could bring them back alive."

McDonald argued, told what he had done in other places against law breakers, but the deputy was not convinced.

"Why, if a man got a drop on one," he said, "the others living miles away would hear about it and get the drop on him. Nothing but a company of soldiers could halfway do the job."

McDonald snorted in disgust. "I don't need a company, but I do need a few real he-men."

"Go out in town and get them," advised the deputy. "You have my permission to do that."

"That's exactly what I'll do." He stormed out of the office.

But he could convince nobody. He telegraphed the main deputy at Topeka, who came. The two tried to persuade a dozen deputies. The main deputy even told about what a reputation for skill and daring McDonald had as a Ranger and deputy marshal in Texas. But it was no use. They would not follow anybody.

McDonald said angrily, "A brave bunch they are! If I can get just one man with nerve enough to drive a hack, I'll go. And I'll bring it back loaded with criminals."

He finally found a man who agreed to drive, but who made it quite clear what his part would be.

"Now I'm not to do any fighting. Me an' my hack will stay out of rifle range. You bring 'em to the hack handcuffed and I'll haul 'em," he said. McDonald grimly agreed.

They set out before daylight in a large, three-seated vehicle pulled by two horses, with one extra mount for McDonald. They drove to the home of the most desperate character in the gang, who lived in a dugout in a small clearing. It was barely daybreak. Scarcely a breath of air was stirring when McDonald slipped across the clearing with his Winchester and pushed open the door without knocking.

A woman stepped in front of him and gave a warning cry to a man on the bed, who reached for a gun. With a quick motion McDonald pushed aside the woman and covered the man.

"Drop it, or you're a dead man!" was his order. There was no mistaking the meaning in that crisp voice. The outlaw's gun clattered to the floor and the hands that had held it were

handcuffed. Two minutes later the astonished hack driver saw the pair coming.

"Delivery number one!" McDonald announced in a matter-of-fact voice. "Now let's round up the others."

In a few cases the men fled, but a well-directed bullet, together with a stern command to halt, stopped them. At one house two were taken at the breakfast table. At another, a criminal jumped on his horse but quickly dismounted and surrendered. The alarm was not spread, for the houses were long distances apart. Gunfire was too common to be excited about, and Bill McDonald worked rapidly. By the time the second group was marched up, the hack driver had gained courage. He kept closer behind to see the fun.

The outlaws, once they were caught, were inclined to be sociable, even to joke about the matter.

"Why, hello Jim!" was the greeting given one fresh prisoner as he walked up to the hack handcuffed. "You been buying fruit trees, too, I see. Was it apples, peaches, or pears?"

"It was sour grapes," Jim replied, his face half a grin, half a scowl.

"Hope it's not a tree with a rope tied to one of its limbs," a third captive volunteered cheerfully.

What a busy day! McDonald's favorite hour of dawn had soon passed, but the work was going too well to stop. He had captured his eight men and rounded up an extra one—an outlaw who happened to be visiting his brother-in-law at the wrong time.

The loaded hack, all three seats full, entered town the next morning with the driver sitting on the knees of two prisoners. The dreaded Sand Creek gang had been rounded up in a single day by a single man—with not a drop of blood spilled.

Within a few days the prisoners were on their way to the various places where they were wanted for their assortment of crimes. The Guthrie men, who at first had refused to go with him, were now eager for adventure.

"Make another roundup," they told McDonald. "The next time you'll have plenty of help."

"No, you fellows are a little too slow," he told them with a ghost of a smile. Then in his well-known drawl he added, "My deliveries in this region have all been made."

— *J. A. Rickard*

Things to Do

1. Where was the Cherokee Strip? Locate it on a map of the United States. Read the description of the Strip from the story.
2. Read aloud, from the story, the answers to the following questions:
   a. Why did McDonald want a badge of a United States marshal?
   b. How did McDonald prepare for his journey into the strip?
   c. How did he cover up the fact that he was an officer?
   d. How did he win the confidence of the outlaws?
   e. How did they receive him?
   f. Why did McDonald promise "spring delivery" on his fruit trees?
   g. Why was not the sheriff willing to help McDonald when he had located the outlaws?
   h. How did the marshal finally decide to arrest and bring in the criminals?
   i. How did the outlaws behave when they recognized each other in the hack?

Today the Texas Ranger is mainly an officer to keep the peace; but about 1850, when this poem was written, he was also a warrior. Indeed, he had just distinguished himself in the war between the United States and Mexico; perhaps the writer had this in mind when he wrote the poem. Rangers also helped win independence for Texas.

The Texas Ranger

Mount, mount and away on the green prairies,
The sword is our scepter, the fleet steed our pride!
Up, up with our flag! let its bright folds gleam out.
Mount, mount and away on the wild border scout.

We care not for danger, we heed not the foe,
Where our gallant steed bears us, right onward we go;
And never as cowards shall we fly from the fight,
While our belts bear a blade, and our Star sheds its light.

Then mount and away—give our horses the rein,
The Ranger's at home on the prairies again.
Spur, spur for the chase, dash on to the fight—
Cry Vengeance for Texas—and God speed the right.

The clouds of the foe gather thick round our way,
Our war-cry rings out as we rush to the fray.
What to us is the fear of the death-giving plain?
We've braved it before, and we'll brave it again.

— J. T. Lytle

A Texas Ranger's Story

This story was told by a young man who joined the Texas Rangers near San Saba nearly one hundred years ago. The Indians had made a raid into a white settlement and killed three members of a family. Two children — a boy and a girl — were captured and taken away. Frank Gholson, the young Ranger, was sent to help rescue the children. Here is his story:

We learned that the murdered people were members of the Jackson family, and that there should be two more children, a girl and a boy. While the funeral services went on, a careful search was made for the children, but no sign of them could we find.

The Indians had divided into two groups. A small group, afoot and with only one horse, went directly east. A larger mounted group went south, down the Colorado River. They took the Jackson family's horses also.

We followed them as far as the San Saba Peak, where we halted. Even though we were well mounted, they had the advantage of us; for we could follow their trail only in the daylight, but they could travel both day and night. We returned north and went to the supply camp for more provisions, men, and pack mules. We

divided our men into small groups to cover the country thoroughly. In this way we hoped to meet the Indians as they returned from their killing and robbing.

On the night of November 6, 1858, eight of us struck the trail where the Indians had passed along earlier in the night. We followed it half a mile or more and discovered some pieces of cloth that we took to be parts of the white girl's clothing. The two children evidently were on one horse, which was loose in the herd with no rope, bridle, or other means to guide it. This we could tell from the crooked course the horse made.

We were sure that we were on a hot trail. Second Lieutenant, Gideon P. Cowan, sent three of the men east to tell the other Rangers and bring help.

This left only five of our party to follow the trail. We found where the Indians had stopped to water their horses, and we discovered very plainly where the little girl had been allowed to get off the horse, and walk along the narrow sandbar of a branch. We saw where she had knelt down and drunk. Her tracks were plain, and no other horse tracks were near enough to erase them. We supposed she had left a plain trail on purpose for us to follow. The boy's tracks puzzled us. We could see only one track. We

felt sure it was the boy's track but felt that he must be crippled, for he made only one track in a place. We later learned that he had lost one boot.

We continued the trail all day. About four in the afternoon our three men caught up with us, and later we saw six men coming up the trail behind us. We halted to let them catch up and they halted too, thinking we might be Indians. One of our men waved a white handkerchief on a stick and held up his broad brimmed hat, which Indians never wore. When they came up we learned they were men who had lost some horses in Lampasas and Burnet Counties.

Lieutenant Cowan told them, "We are Rangers, and members of Captain John Williams's company. I am his Second Lieutenant, and we are on the trail of a number of stolen horses and two captive children. We mean to spare no time, to use all the judgment possible, to travel day and night, and bear any hardships or danger, for the sake of those children. If you want to go with us and will not in any way delay us; if you will do as we do, fare as we fare, and obey as my men do, we will be glad to have you."

They agreed to these rules, and we all moved on. After crossing a pecan bayou we stopped and ate supper and grazed our horses awhile. One of the men who joined the company had a watch, and from then on we worked on time. Lieutenant Cowan showed us a star and said to us, "That is the way the Indians are going. Two of you take the lead and follow in the direction of that star."

We started in the direction of the star, traveling until midnight without stopping. We came to where the Indians had stopped to cook something to eat. We also stopped about two hours, grazed our horses, and went on.

When daylight came we started off in a V formation. We traveled in pairs, in the form of a figure V, a mile or more wide at the opening. Each pair of men was several hundred yards from his nearest neighbor but in calling distance. In this way, any word could be passed up and down the line. Soon two men in the lead at the right found the trail and passed back the news. In the afternoon we came to a place where the Indians had stopped and cooked again, and we also stopped a couple of hours. Our next stop was about eleven o'clock that night, when we again rested one and one-half hours.

When daylight came we found that we were right on top of the trail. Cowan told Tom Potts and me, who did most of the trailing, to follow the trail. We were traveling west, north of a range of mountains—a lone mountain standing off north of the main range. The Indians had passed between the main mountains and this one. Tom and I were eighty yards ahead of the rest of the company. We looked up from our work long enough to see a man on a horse on that mountain, facing us. He disappeared, then appeared long enough to count us, and disappeared again, this time for good.

We told Lieutenant Cowan what we had seen. He gave orders for us to gallop in close formation, telling us that this rider was the rear guard and the rest of the Indians were not far off. He told Tom and me to keep our eyes on the trail.

Someone from the rear called out, "Yonder they are!—away out in front!"

I looked up long enough to see a long string of horses, being driven on the run. The next I heard was, "They are getting ready to fight! They are rounding up that herd!" But we soon discovered that they were roping fresh horses from the herd.

Some yelled, "Look yonder! Two foot Indians are leaving the rest of them!"

By this time we were in a run. Cowan told Tom and me to give up the trail, and we gladly did so.

Cowan then said, "I will take part of the men and run in between the foot Indians and the horse herd. Rome, you take the other part and run in front of the foot Indians and keep them from going to the mountains, and let's get them first."

We divided, and I followed Cowan. Before we could get up to them the two figures that we were pursuing hid. In a few moments one of them rose from his hiding place, and I heard him say, "They're white men! They're white men! I see their hats, and I see their stirrups!"

He popped up and stayed up, and we soon saw that he was no Indian but a white boy. Some of the men jumped from their horses and ran up to where the two had been hiding. Everyone was excited, for we realized they were the two children we had been looking for. One of the men ran up to the girl, who was almost faint from starvation and excitement. Another man began

Bill Neale

to shout in camp-meeting style, praising God for letting the children be rescued.

Then suddenly someone noticed that the Indians had disappeared, and we knew they had given up the prisoners to save their own hides. It was the smartest trick that I have ever seen a bunch of Indians play, and it let them get away without the loss of a man.

The children were fed and cared for at Camp Colorado by some white women until they were recovered. Kind settlers adopted them, and both grew to manhood and womanhood. I feel sure, however, that they never forgot their rescue by the Rangers.

— *Benjamin Franklin Gholson*

Things to Do

1. How did the Rangers know the Indians had the girl and boy prisoners?
2. How did they pick up their trail later?
3. How did they know the horse was not being led?
4. How do you know the Rangers were skilled trailers?
5. Where did the Rangers first see the Indians they were following?
6. What trick did the Indians use to keep from being captured?
7. From what you know of Texas Rangers, how was their work in the story different from the things they do today?

Cowboy Stories
A Real Cowboy

Jim looked wistfully at his Uncle Fred and the two cowboys, as they mounted their horses to start out for the day. "May I go along too?" he asked.

Uncle Fred shook his head with some regret. "We have hard work to do today — real cowboy work. As soon as you learn how to ride, I'll take you out with me. But this cowboy work is hard."

Jim was so disappointed that a lump came into his throat. In some ways he was greatly enjoying his vacation on Uncle Fred's New Mexico ranch. It was different from his crowded city home, for here he could look miles in every direction yet not see a house except the ranch headquarters. He liked to watch the white-faced cows and frisky calves and see the cowboys chase them on wiry ponies. But he did so want to be a real cowboy too!

Aunt Peggy helped him. She said, "You can use my saddle and ride Old Pinto."

Old Pinto, Jim soon learned, was the gentlest horse on the ranch and he knew all about cows. The saddle was not much too large, and on it was a rope with a loop in one end, like the cowboys used.

In a week he was riding all over the place; in another week he was roping fence posts and going five miles to a country store and post office on the highway for the mail and groceries.

Aunt Peggy now helped him more: "You can drive up the milk cows every afternoon," she told him. She went with him the first day, but afterwards he went by himself.

One afternoon he found only three of the four cows he had been driving in each day. He started them toward the ranch, then turned back to look for the missing cow.

Ten minutes later he found her under a large tree. With her was a newborn calf, so tiny and weak that its legs wobbled when it tried to stand up. How could it even walk?

He looked back toward the ranch house two miles away. Then he glanced at the setting sun. He knew the little animal couldn't walk that far. If he left them, he would surely have trouble finding them again. Only last night he had heard Uncle Fred talking about how bad the wolves were, and how they sometimes killed newborn calves when they found them at night. He doubted if he could carry the calf two miles on foot. He would have to take it home on Pinto.

But when he tried to catch it, the mother cow bellowed and shook her horns at him. He tried talking to her, as he had seen his Aunt Peggy do.

"So-o-o-o, cow," he coaxed, but the old cow kept shaking her horns.

"Maybe I had better rope her and tie her to the tree," he reasoned to himself. "Then I can take the calf home and come back for her later."

He unlooped the rope from the saddle and straightened it out. Swinging it around and around, as he had seen cowboys do, and as he had practiced over and over again, he threw it toward the mother cow. It landed squarely over her horns the first throw.

Not until he had tied her head up close to the tree could he touch the calf. Even then the cow bawled and pulled on the rope when the

calf gave a faint, "Baa-a-a!"

For a while it looked as though Old Pinto might give some trouble, too. He pricked up his ears and moved away when Jim tried to go up to him with the calf in his arms. But the boy let him smell the newcomer, and he stood still after that.

Jim had to lift twice before he could swing the calf up on the horse. He was glad now that Aunt Peggy's saddle was large. Using one hand to steady the calf in the saddle, he held the reins and pulled himself up with the other. Then he said, "Get up!" to Old Pinto.

It was slow going, for the calf wiggled and twisted. But Old Pinto seemed to know just

what to do. He picked his steps carefully over the rough ground and walked slowly as he started out.

They were almost halfway home. Jim was beginning to think his troubles were over, when the calf gave a sudden jump and fell off, taking Jim with him.

The fall stunned the boy, causing him to let go the calf. Into a nearby thicket the animal darted. It was five minutes before Jim could catch it again. Old Pinto stood watching and looking as if he wanted to help.

It seemed that the little animal was stronger, or Jim was growing weaker, for now he could not keep it on the horse long enough to mount behind it. After he had tried three times, failing each time, he gave the faithful Pinto a slap on the hip and started him toward the ranch house.

"Maybe they will come for me when Old Pinto walks in without a rider," he said to himself.

He tried carrying the calf in his arms, but it was so heavy that he had to stop to rest every fifty feet or so.

He kept wondering if Old Pinto had reached home. Maybe he had stopped to eat grass instead of going on. He watched the red sun go out of sight, knowing it would soon be dark. Unless someone came soon, he would be out all night.

A noise behind him caused him to turn around to look. Toward him in an awkward run came the old mother cow, bawling at every step. He must not have tied the rope tightly enough to the tree, for it was dragging behind her. The calf struggled in his arms and went "Baa-a-a!" Its mother answered and ran all the faster.

She looked so excited and fierce as she came bounding toward him that he felt every bit of his courage slipping away. But he had seen Uncle Fred carry calves in his arms. Jim knew that if he was going to learn to be a cowboy, he must do as other cowboys would do.

So he held on to the calf, putting it between

him and the cow. When she reached it, she began licking it and mooing happily. She did not seem to notice Jim.

As for the calf, it showed them in a minute what it wanted. With one dive it reached its mother's udder, and soon it was sucking and butting with its tiny red and white head to get more milk.

Jim was not afraid now, for the cow kept licking her baby's neck and mooing. Presently the calf's sides bulged. Foam dripped from its mouth, as it changed from one teat to another. Finally, it stopped nursing. All this time Jim had stood by patiently.

The calf was heavier now, when he picked it up and started walking again, but it no longer wiggled in his arms. It even reached out a rough little tongue to lick the side of his neck as he walked along. The mother followed.

It was almost dark by the time he started out again, and he was pretty tired. He certainly was glad to hear Uncle Fred's voice calling him and to see him ride up, leading Old Pinto.

"Well, well, Mr. Cowboy, I see you are bringing in a new calf."

"Yes, sir. Isn't that what you would have done?" asked Jim anxiously.

"Yes indeed," replied his uncle quickly, "and you have done it as well as I could have done it, too. But you must be tired. Let me carry the calf a while and you ride Old Pinto."

The tall man leaned over and took the calf out of Jim's arms. Old Pinto stuck out his nose to welcome the boy before Jim climbed into the saddle.

"Yes, sir, that was a good job, well done," Uncle Fred repeated, as they neared the ranch house lights. "And it makes you a real cowboy, too. If you do one job well, you can be trusted to do other jobs. How would you like to go with me tomorrow to help round up cattle?"

Jim almost lost his voice at first, but finally he said, "I would like it fine, sir."

— J. A. Rickard

Things to Do

1. In this story Jim solved four problems that were very important to him. These problems were as follows:
   a. Learning to ride and use a rope.
   b. Deciding how to take the newborn calf home.
   c. Deciding what to do when the calf fell off the horse.
   d. Protecting himself when the cow broke loose from the tree.
2. Tell how Jim solved each of these problems. Make a list of words that describe the kind of boy he must have been.
3. How was Jim rewarded for solving his problems well?

Becoming a Cowboy

The Wagoner family moved from their city home to their Rainbow Ranch in the early summer. The father, Bob Wagoner, had once been a cowboy, but the twelve-year-old son, Roger, had never lived anywhere but in the city. On his second day at their new home he announced, "I want a pony, and I want to learn to ride him."

"That's right," nodded Bob from across the breakfast table. "Folks around here would laugh at a boy who couldn't ride and handle a horse.

That's why I bought that little black horse for you."

"And will you help me learn today?" the boy asked eagerly.

"I have to ride up the country to see about finding a pasture for those new cows. But Slim here is an old hand with horses, and he won't need to go with me. I'll turn you over to him."

Thirty minutes later the two were at the barn, Roger eager but Slim slow-moving and unexcited. They chose the smallest of three saddles hanging on pegs, and the old cowboy shortened the stirrups so that the boy could reach them with his feet. Slim then handed Roger a bridle.

"The next job is to catch your pony and bridle and saddle him," he announced. "Maybe they are small enough. I've taken them up as much as I can."

Roger took the bridle and started slowly out into the barnyard, where Jet was standing. But the horse seemed afraid of him. Try as he might Roger could not get close enough to put the bridle over the animal's ears. He was almost ready to ask for help when Slim called out from the shadow of the barn, "Come and get this rope. He doesn't know you well enough to let you catch him."

Roger took the loop in his right hand and the coil in his left. He crept toward the pony, not stopping till he was within fifteen feet of him. He slung the rope around and around and threw it toward Jet's head. The animal snorted, dodged, and galloped off to the far side of the barnyard. Slim had to come to his aid.

"Don't sling it around your head," he warned patiently. "That scares animals. Drag it on the ground until you are ready to throw the loop, then do it without any lost motion."

Roger tried, and Jet did not dodge this time; but the rope missed his head completely. The boy was becoming discouraged, when Slim gently took the rope.

"Now watch me," he said.

It seemed easy when he did it. Jet did not even jump when the loop settled down over his head, although he was a bit nervous as the two advanced slowly toward him.

This time Roger had trouble with the bridle. Jet's head was too high for him to reach his ears, so Slim had to pull it down for the boy. The animal seemed sensitive about those ears. When the bridle went over one of them he jerked his head, the bridle falling to the ground. Slim picked it up and put it on Jet.

"It's a good idea to bridle the ear farthest from you first," he explained as he did the bridling. "And be careful how you handle the ears. Some animals are touchy that way. Now we'll saddle him up."

Roger managed to put the blanket on straight, but the saddle was almost too heavy for him to handle. The first time he threw it on Jet's back a stirrup doubled up under it. While trying to straighten it out, he dragged the blanket out of place. Slim took charge and straightened out saddle and blanket. Then he reached under the horse's body to draw the girth to him.

"I'll do this, and you can watch," he said. Roger watched and thought he would know the next time how to tighten the girth.

He was sure he knew how to mount — he had watched his father do that several times: he approached the horse on the left side; took the reins, then the saddle horn, in his left hand; placed his left foot in the stirrup and his right hand on the cantle; then vaulted into the saddle.

"Now let him go," he ordered.

Slim turned loose the bridle bit and stepped aside. Jet started off uncertainly. The man opened the gate, and the horse trotted through it. Roger circled him around after he had gone a hundred yards out on the prairie, then headed him back toward the gate. The animal was behaving nicely, and Roger was getting ready to hear the approval of his cowboy teacher.

But that approval did not come. As Jet neared the gate, a frisky calf made a dash for it

also. Straight toward horse and rider he came.
Jet jumped sidewise, and Roger went sprawling
on the ground.

He scrambled to his feet, to be greeted by
a loud, "Haw, haw!" It came from Slim, who
seemed to be enjoying the scene immensely.
Roger was making such little progress that the
laughter of his friend annoyed him.

"I don't see anything funny about it," he
stormed out, as he tried to keep his temper. Slim

had caught the pony and was holding him by the bridle reins. He stopped laughing quickly.

"Maybe not, son," he admitted, "but you're supposed to laugh when a real cowboy is thrown from his horse. Everybody does it."

"Well, I don't know all about riding, and I don't like to be laughed at when I'm doing my best."

"I'll try not to laugh at you again. I'll tell you one thing, though. You'll never make a real rancher until you can grin and take it."

He turned and led the pony into the barn. Roger was half glad that his mother called him at that moment.

When he went back to the barn after the noon meal, Slim had ridden out to the pasture. He looked at Jet a full minute and walked away. He was very unhappy.

Bob was back home before sundown the next day. Roger said nothing about his trouble with Jet, but his mother, Ellen, had seen him thrown off, and of course she would tell his father the whole story. They were good parents, and he knew he would have another chance; but he would not be able to go on his first cattle drive, as he had hoped. Bob announced at the supper table that he had leased a pasture, and he and Slim would start to it with the herd the very next day.

Roger did not ask to go, but just before leaving, Slim said to the boy, "Now remember — a gen-u-ine cowboy laughs when he is thrown from a horse. Then he gets up and rides him!"

Before Roger could think of a reply, Bob added, "With good luck we ought to be getting back home by four o'clock tomorrow. We'll come back by the Buffalo Pass route, in case you and Jet should take a notion to meet us."

Then and there Roger knew what he was going to do that day. The herd was barely out of sight when he went to the barn. He took his pocket knife and made two new holes that allowed him to take up the stirrups another notch. Now, he thought, they were just the right length; and he tried out the saddle on the fence to be sure.

The next hour or two he spent practicing roping. He chose a hitching post in one corner of the barnyard. With a medium-sized loop in his rope, trailing behind him, he crept toward the post. One time he missed it entirely, but in all the other trials he settled the rope around the post without any trouble. He was so interested that Ellen had to call him three times for dinner.

While he was eating, she asked, "Are you going to ride Jet this afternoon?"

He looked up quickly, but she was busy taking up some beans. Finally he answered,

"Yes, ma'am — thought I would try it."

"Well, I'll be around the house. If you need help, just whistle."

"Er — thanks. But I think I can manage." Now he knew that she was on his side. It made him feel better to know that she was going to let him work out his problem without being watched.

He found Jet munching hay in his stall, with a halter and a short rope on his head. He backed out in fear when Roger came closer. For thirty minutes Roger followed the horse around the barnyard, trying to get hold of the short rope. At times it seemed as if Jet would let the boy capture him, but always when Roger reached out his hand he shied away.

Finally Roger uncoiled the long rope he had used on the hitching post that morning. He remembered everything that he had been told. He was not to sling the loop over his head; he was to slip up gently, and he was to be as quiet as possible when throwing it over the pony's head.

At the very first throw he succeeded. Jet seemed frightened at first, but when Roger gently but firmly tightened the loop around his neck, he stayed quiet, not moving in his tracks. Speaking in a low voice and edging closer by short steps, Roger in two minutes was stroking Jet's neck. Instead of bolting in fear, the animal was now looking around with interest at this stranger.

Putting on the bridle was as hard a job as catching the horse had been. Roger finally brought up a chicken trough, turned it upside down, and stood on it. Jet jerked his head at the touch of the bridle, throwing the boy off balance. He tried again, and this time he looped both ears inside the encircling bridle. In another minute the bit was in his mouth and the leather throat-latch was buckled on the left side of the pony's head. Jet chewed on the loose bit, but he followed willingly when Roger led him to the barn where the saddle was hanging.

The saddle blanket was already folded double, so that all he had to do was to put it on the horse's back the long way. To prevent trouble with the stirrups, such as he had had before, Roger hooked the far stirrup over the saddle horn. He tried twice before he got the twenty-pound saddle in the right place. The lacing up of the girth was fairly easy. Jet snorted once when it was drawn tight, but the boy thought it was a satisfied snort, and not one of fear.

He now led the pony outside, closed the gate, and fastened it. No unruly calf would upset plans this time. He led Jet fifteen yards from the gate, stopped, gathered the reins in his hand and, as gently as he could, climbed into the saddle.

The rest of it was easy. Jet responded quickly when Roger pressed his sides with his legs, and started off in a trot. Roger pulled back on the reins and brought him to a walk. For an hour he slowly rode back and forth across the pasture in sight of home. Gradually the boy lost his nervousness. He urged the pony into a trot, and into a gallop, then pulled him down to a walk again.

He could not resist the temptation to ride down to the house. After throwing the reins over the hitching post, as he had seen Bob do, he strode up to the front porch. Solemnly he knocked on the door, and almost at once his mother opened it. Renolyn was with her, carrying her doll, Sue, and ready to talk, as usual.

"We saw you! We saw you ride him!" the little sister cried gleefully, by way of greeting. Then she added, "And it's our turn next."

Roger was so happy that he would have been willing to take the girl and doll for a ride, then and there, but Ellen smilingly interfered.

"We'd better wait awhile for that," she cautioned. "Maybe so — before long."

Roger agreed, but not for long did he remain off the back of his pony. He recalled Bob's invitation for him to ride out to meet them at four o'clock, and thirty minutes ahead of time he had his pony's head pointing toward the northwest. Proudly, and almost impatiently, he sat on his pony on a hill overlooking Buffalo Pass.

Bob and Slim exclaimed at the sight of him, but he had a feeling that they were not greatly surprised. Perhaps they had even expected him. They gave him a center place between them as they rode along toward home, and they asked him a lot of questions. Jet had to take extra steps to keep pace with the two larger horses, but he kept up with them. Roger sat just a little straighter in his saddle than either of the men.

Maybe that was because he was not so tired. Maybe it was because he was so happy.

— J. A. Rickard

Things to Do

1. What problem was Roger trying to solve?
2. What did the old cowboy, Slim, mean when he said, "You are supposed to laugh when a real cowboy is thrown from his horse?"
3. Make a list of the things that Roger did in learning to ride a horse. Do you think he chose intelligent ways to learn to ride?
4. What was Roger's reward for solving his problem?

A West Texas Roundup

Before the use of fences on ranches in the West, the roundup was a time of hard, careful work and much excitement. This is a true story of a Texas roundup in 1894, but the names are fictitious.

"Well, boys, our boss has been chosen to head the spring roundup."

Thus did Shorty Brown break the news of the honor that had come to their own foreman, Big Joe Ketchum, after the two had returned from the April meeting of cattlemen at Big Spring in 1894.

The other boys of the Lazy L Ranch were very proud of their boss. Sandy Smith wanted to take a day off to celebrate, and Irish Donovan seconded the motion. But Big Joe was too modest to be so honored.

"There's too much work to do now," he told them, "for this roundup will be held in two or three weeks, and we have to get ready for it."

Big Joe himself took three days to see some of the ranch owners of the region. He wanted them to set the time and place for the start. When he returned, he reported that it would begin the last week in May.

The first roundup spot was about fifteen

Longhorn Cattle Roundup at Fort Griffin State Park

miles from the Lazy L headquarters, in the brakes below the Cap Rock. To the north and west lay the Staked Plains, with its rich grazing land, smooth as a floor, and its nine-ranch division headquarters. Below the Cap Rock to the south and east were the lower rough lands with their mesquite trees, dry creek beds, canyons, and scrubby bushes. It was too rough for farming, but it offered livestock good protection from winter winds.

Joe and the other ranch foremen did not like fences. The barbed wire had been invented, but it was not in general use. At the Lazy L headquarters there was a small, fenced pasture for the horses and a few milk cows; and on the north side there was a drift fence to keep cattle from going too far south in cold weather.

Otherwise the range was open. It was not uncommon for a Lazy L cow to roam fifty miles from her range, and cattle all mixed together from many ranches were scattered over the country. It was the job of the roundup men to gather the cattle and return them to the ranchmen who owned them. By late May many new calves would have been born, and these were given the brands of their mothers.

By late May also the steers had gained some flesh from eating the spring grass, and some of them were ready to be sold. So Ketchum's men had to select a central spot, drive up and brand the livestock near, and separate from the herd all cattle selected for the market. When a certain spot was worked out, the roundup would move on to the next location.

As the first roundup spot was nearest the Lazy L headquarters, there was a dance on Saturday night at that place. They had a cowboy fiddler, a huge table groaning with good things to eat, and much square dancing. If there happened to be a shortage of ladies, one or two cowboys tied handkerchiefs on their arms and posed as ladies for the dance.

For the roundup proper, each ranch furnished from three to five men for driving in the cattle. Each ranch had its own chuck wagon, cook, branding men, and remuda boy. It was this boy's business to look after the horses, for each rider had about eight mounts. The outfits were camped about five hundred yards apart.

Time out for coffee on Waggoner Ranch

Little Joe Ketchum, fifteen year old son of the Lazy L foreman, was the remuda boy for his group. Some of the horses were hobbled to keep them from wandering off, but a few were staked with ropes tied to stakes or pegs that were driven into the ground. The others were turned loose, but they stayed close by. Each morning Little Joe went out before daylight and drove them into a corral made of ropes stretched on shrubs or stakes. There each cowboy caught his own mount for the day.

The cook presided over the chuck wagon. It was an ordinary canvas-covered farm wagon with shelves built high in the back end. Covering the shelves was a broad door with hinges at the bottom and legs at each top corner. When this door was opened and the legs were stretched out to stand on the ground, a rude table was made. The cook's main "weapons" were a skillet and a large coffee pot, plus a covered "dutch" oven for cooking beans and other foods. Tin

Courtesy Texas Highway Department
Skillet, Coffee Pot and Bean Pot on the Mathews Ranch near Albany, Texas

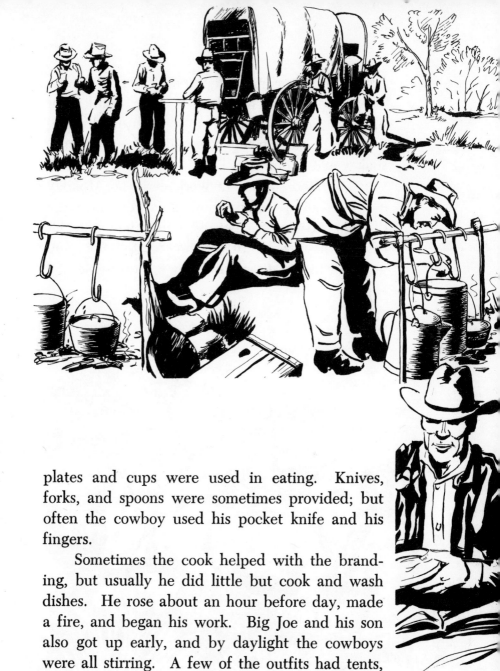

plates and cups were used in eating. Knives, forks, and spoons were sometimes provided; but often the cowboy used his pocket knife and his fingers.

Sometimes the cook helped with the branding, but usually he did little but cook and wash dishes. He rose about an hour before day, made a fire, and began his work. Big Joe and his son also got up early, and by daylight the cowboys were all stirring. A few of the outfits had tents, but most of the men slept on the open prairie. They had blankets and used their saddles for pillows. Some spread their ropes around them, for they believed ropes would keep off rattlesnakes and tarantulas.

The men started to work early on Monday morning, groups of cowboys going out in every direction to look for cattle. Once they were located, they were driven in to the roundup grounds, in groups of fifty cows, more or less.

There the bawling, milling herd was inspected, and all unbranded cattle given their proper marks. It was the job of certain cowboys to "cut out" of the herd those cattle not yet branded. It was hard work, and sometimes a cowboy had to change mounts several times during the day. He rode into the herd, picked out a calf, and drove it with its mother to the branding place. There the calf was either roped, or seized bare-handed and thrown down and branded.

Great care had to be taken to get the marks in exactly the right place and at the correct angle. The Lazy L brand, for instance, had to be applied on the right hip, just below the level of the hip bone, at an angle of forty-five degrees from straight up. All brands were registered with the county clerk, and with the Texas Cattlemen's Association.

As calves were branded, a man kept tally and called out the marks on each animal. Such a man needed to be honest and accurate, and

Courtesy Texas Highway Department
Branding on the Mosier Ranch west of Amarillo, Texas

Courtesy Texas Highway Department
Ready for Chow at the Mathews Ranch

able to speak clearly in a loud voice, for the owners kept tally also. He called out, "Lazy L, one calf," "Circle D, one calf," and so on through the day.

Although the branding was painful, a growing calf's burn would heal within two or three weeks; yet he bawled with all his might during the operation. Sometimes the mother cow came to the rescue of her baby. The cowboys kept her some fifty yards away under guard, but occasionally she slipped by them.

At this roundup Irish Donovan had a narrow escape from an enraged mother cow. He was

branding her calf when he heard warning yells from companions, who were scattering in all directions. When he looked up, he saw the angry cow bearing down upon him six feet away. He dodged, but the cow's horn caught his pants' leg and ripped it. The cow ran through the fire and turned for another charge, but a rope thrown over her horns stopped her. She went off licking the back of her branded calf. The cowboys enjoyed the experience; to them it was the high spot of the whole roundup.

It was in the "cutting out" of the cattle that the cowboy could best show off his trained horse. Shorty Brown boasted that his horse could read his mind. Certainly the pony seemed to know what animal the rider wanted; and when she did not move along fast enough, he sometimes reached over and bit her back to make her hurry. A light pressure of Shorty's knee or a flick of one bridle rein was all that "Old Paint" needed to go after the right cow.

The cow was always cut out of the herd with her calf, so that everyone would know what brand it should have. Sometimes in the milling herd the mother and calf were separated. The calf would sometimes follow the wrong mother, but the cow always knew her offspring. If the mother had died when the calf was young, or if the two otherwise became separated permanently, the calf was called a "dogie." Sandy Smith defined a dogie as a calf "that has no mammy and doesn't know where its pappy is."

Some unbranded older cattle turned up. All of them were divided proportionately among the different ranches, or they became the property of the Cattlemen's Association. If there were many unbranded older stock, they were driven into a long narrow chute and branded standing up. It was both troublesome and dangerous to throw them down.

For three days this hot work continued. Then the roundup groups moved to another location to repeat their work. Four different stands were made during the ten or twelve days that the work went on.

Finally, the last cow was branded, and the Lazy L and other outfits drove their herds nearer home or to market.

During that time the men had slept on the prairie, kept company with rattlesnakes, breathed dust until they were nearly stifled, and smelled scorched hair until at times they were almost sick. They had worked and sweated and had worn out both themselves and their ponies.

But they had met old friends and made new ones. Each ranch owner knew how many animals bore his brand, and he could figure his gains or losses. To the cowboys and to the ranch owners, therefore, roundup time was the busiest and best time of the year.

— *J. A. Rickard*

Things to Do

1. What proof is there that spring roundups were arranged by all the cattlemen concerned?
2. Why were roundups held?
3. What different types of work were done at roundups?

4. If you were a remuda boy, what would you expect to do?
5. What dangers were there about roundup work?
6. Why was it necessary to brand cattle?
7. Why was roundup time looked forward to, by both ranch owners and cowboys?
8. Find the sentences in the order in which the events happened in the story. Rereading will help you.

   a. Big Joe went to see the ranch owners.
   b. There was a dance on Saturday night at the first roundup spot.
   c. The cattle were driven into the roundup grounds, in groups of fifty cows or more.
   d. All of the unbranded cattle were branded.
   e. A man kept tally and called out the brand of each animal.
   f. A cowboy could best show off his trained horse in the cutting out of the cattle.
   g. Sometimes the mother cow came to the rescue of her baby that was being branded.
   h. Four different stands were made during the ten days of the branding.
   i. Each cowboy had made new friends and met old ones.
   j. The ranch owner knew how many cattle that he had.

Alone on the Range

This story took place in southeastern New Mexico several years before the beginning of the present century — a time when communication between people in the towns and those in the country and between those living on ranches was different from what it is today. Automobiles, telephones, airplanes, and radios now have brought people and places much closer together.

On that November morning George Reynolds and his mother stood together on the porch of their ranch house. Across the far-flung acres that stretched before their eyes, the sun was rising, touching the fog-filled valley with a silvery mist; and beyond, in the distance, were the purple Guadalupe Mountains.

But neither was thinking of the peace and beauty of the scene that lay before them. George's young face was eager, alert; Elta's eyes were filled with doubt and anxiety.

"But Father told me to be sure to go after our cattle by Thursday if he didn't get home in time, Mother," George urged. "Zeb Conners will go with me. He's old, but he's as trusty and safe on the range as Father himself."

"I know that," agreed Elta. "Zeb will be glad enough to do us a favor. Your father has

helped him out of many tight places. Zeb's always said there was nothing he wouldn't do for
us."

"Then what are you worrying about?" asked
the boy.

"I don't quite know," Elta replied doubtfully. "You're only twelve. You've never been
away overnight without your father. Someway

I'm afraid to let you go." After a moment or two she added, "Maybe it's only a woman's intuition, or perhaps it's just a mother's fears."

"Then I may go?" George asked.

"Ye-es," she replied, still doubtfully. "Since your father planned it this way, I'm sure it will come out all right."

Though there was a mist in her eyes, she smiled cheerfully at her son.

A short time later George was on his way to the range, stopping midway for Zeb Conners.

George realized how important his mission was. Although it was November, it was still hot — unseasonably hot. Because the good weather might be over any day, the cattle must be brought in before the fall storms came.

Nat Reynolds had gone to Albuquerque to arrange for a loan. He was depending on the sale of cattle to make a necessary payment on their land, George knew. The boy couldn't understand why his mother should worry. Zeb was entirely reliable; and although he was old, he was one of the most experienced cattlemen in that part of the country. George felt very grown up and sure of himself as he turned in at Zeb's place.

The old man was at the corral. Seeing George, he walked slowly to the boy, who explained his mission.

Zeb took off his hat and scratched his head. "I dunno how I could manage to go today, Son," he said. "Mandy fell down yesterday and hurt her back. She's sorta laid up and can't get around. It's nothing serious, but I reckon I oughtn't to leave her and the place alone overnight."

George swallowed hard. "No, of course not, Zeb. You shouldn't do that."

The boy spoke with more assurance than he felt, and Zeb's face brightened.

"Tell you what you do, Son. If your pa's not home, come Saturday, you stop by, and I'll go with you then. Mandy'll be able to get around by that time for sure. And this spell of weather'll more'n likely hold out for another few days."

"Thanks a lot, Zeb," George said understandingly. "I hope Mrs. Conners gets along all right."

The boy turned his horse toward home. He was disappointed, and his heart was heavy. After going a short distance, he pulled his horse to a sudden halt.

His father had told him to drive the cattle home from the range not later than Thursday. He was trusting his son to carry out the orders. What if something should happen to the cattle because he delayed going? It might mean a disastrous loss to his parents, one they couldn't stand now. How could anyone have foreseen that Mandy would meet with an accident at this particular time so that Zeb couldn't go along? If he rode back home for his mother's consent to go alone, a day would be lost. Thursday would be past.

The boy sat on his horse, thinking. He tried to sort out his thoughts. His mother wouldn't worry, for she thought Zeb was with him. He hated to go without her permission. Still, he knew the country well; he had often ridden over

the whole range with his father. Though only twelve, he was tall and strong. Blackie, his own horse, was safe, reliable, and well trained to drive cattle —

Suddenly George straightened in the saddle, squared his shoulders. He turned his mount around.

"Come on, boy," he said to Blackie. "We're going to get those cattle — you and I — without Zeb!"

A mile farther on, George pulled on the reins and dismounted. Blackie's saddle girth seemed to be tight. The boy loosened it a notch. The horse turned its head, and George patted it gently.

"We're partners, Blackie! We've a real job to do!" he said.

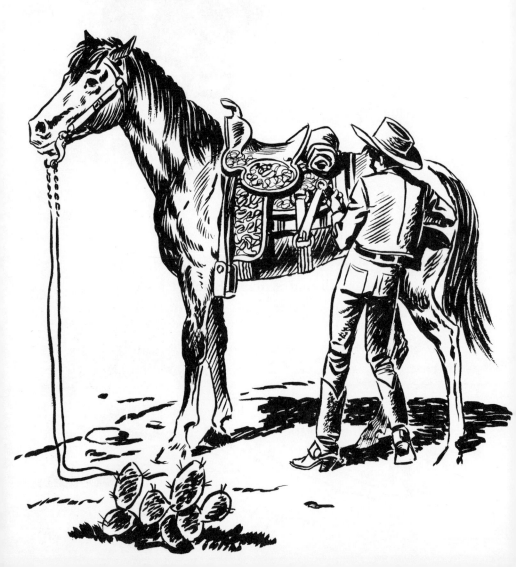

He looked at the roll of bedding that was wrapped in his slicker. He tightened the leather strings that held it behind the cantle. Then, satisfied that all was well, he swung into the saddle and headed northeast. Though there was no good road to guide him, the sun gave him the general direction. He kept his eyes on the tall Guadalupe Peak straight ahead. Sometimes in the low bushy places he lost sight of it, but every time he reached higher ground, there it was — a safe and sure guide.

Blackie was a fast traveler, but the boy pushed him as much as he dared. By the middle of the afternoon they reached the range and

came upon the first of the herd. The rest were not far away. At sundown the cattle had been pretty well rounded up. George counted forty-seven. Feeling sure that was all there were, he dismounted.

"Dinner time and supper time, too, old fellow," he told Blackie as he removed the saddle. "I have some corn for you, and here is fresh grass, too." It was comforting to have Blackie to talk to.

From the black goatskin saddle pockets George took the corn for Blackie and the lunch his mother had prepared. He was tired and hungry; the rest and food were welcome.

Supper over and Blackie staked out, the boy rolled up in his blanket. The range seemed strange and lonely, as if he had never seen it before. From a nearby clump of jack pines a screech owl uttered a sharp cry. The air, stirring slightly, rustled the leaves of the trees, making a continuous whisper. The night seemed alive all around the boy, who was alone on the range for the first time in his life.

George didn't feel a bit grown up now; indeed he felt like a little boy. He thought of his home and his mother. She would be thinking of him, he knew. A lump rose in his throat —a lump as big and hard as a rock in Bad Man's Gulch.

The boy looked up into the velvet blue of the night sky, where millions of low-hanging stars were shining brightly in the clear New Mexico air. It seemed that he could touch them if he stretched his arms upward. Those same stars were shining over his home. Maybe his mother was looking at them, too. This thought comforted him as he turned over, soon to go to sleep.

Early the next morning George lost no time, for he realized that he had a long day of work ahead of him. The way home would be slow. He decided that instead of taking the long trail back, past Zeb's ranch, he would save time by following the old short cut through Deadwood Pass.

In spite of the fact that some of the animals were frisky, George was able to make steady progress. So anxious was he to reach home that by noon Blackie was sweating; and some of the cattle were panting. It was the heat, the boy decided. He had been pushing the herd too fast. He would eat his lunch and let the animals rest.

Unseasonably hot for November, the atmosphere was heavy. Not a breath of air stirred. George noticed that Blackie wasn't enjoying his rest. He was very nervous. When the boy went over to give him a friendly pat on the flank, the horse snorted and jumped about excitedly.

"What's the matter, old fellow?" George asked as he stroked Blackie's velvety nose. "Is this hot weather too much for you? Well, it won't be long now before we'll be home!" he said, more for his own sake than for Blackie's.

George slid into the saddle to start the herd again on its homeward way. But the cattle, too, began to act strangely. Instead of moving along quietly as they had been doing, it seemed as if each of the forty-seven animals wanted to go in a different direction. Sometimes they stopped in little groups, pawing the ground restlessly, raising their heads in the air as if sensing danger. They were bawling more than usual, too. The hot weather, George thought; but he kept them moving in spite of it.

Before long the boy himself became uneasy, feeling as if something were going to happen. He felt tense, almost scared without knowing why. His heart pounded uncomfortably.

Searching the sky, he saw it changing; thin clouds were appearing, gray patches on the blue, like wisps of smoke across the face of the sun. A slight breeze stirred from the northwest. Suddenly the sun went out of sight. All across the northern horizon, stretching like a curtain from east to west, an ominous black cloud rolled forward. It climbed the sky rapidly. With it came a stiff wind, driving dust before it.

George knew — suddenly and with little warning — that before long freezing weather might be upon them. The wind struck with full force. He must keep his cattle together and push them as hard as he could, George told himself. Any cattle separated from the rest might freeze to death, or never be found.

George dismounted, untied his raincoat. In one of the pockets he found a pair of woolen mittens his mother had put there, he thought with a lump in his throat. They felt warm and cheering, for already his fingers were becoming numb. As George climbed back into the saddle, Blackie tossed his head and snorted as if to say that he didn't like the weather any better than did the cattle.

The driving wind made it difficult for the boy to know exactly where he was. But he finally decided that he was about five or six miles from his home slightly to the southwest. The wind was blowing squarely out of the north, which meant that he and Blackie must stay on the left side of the cattle and push them a little to the right. It would not do to let them drift with the wind. Once they reached Deadwood Pass, the way would be less difficult.

But driving the cattle was now no easy matter. The animals seemed to have only one idea — to flee from the cold, biting wind. Sometimes, when they came to a low spot where the wind did not strike them so hard, they wanted to stop. George made his lariat into a whip, cracked it over the backs of the frightened

animals, shouted to them, while Blackie pushed
against them with all his might.   Once the horse
leaned over and bit the neck of a contrary steer.
George pulled sharply on the reins.   "No use
to be mean about it," he told Blackie.

The air continued to grow colder. Rain, turning to sleet, began to fall. George's raincoat kept out the water and some of the cold. But as mile after mile passed, his legs grew stiff. He tried jostling about in the saddle; but this made Blackie nervous. The boy thought of dismounting and walking in order to keep warm. But he couldn't drive the cattle on foot.

Because of the heavy clouds, dark came before sundown. The boy strained his eyes to see the mountain peak, his landmark. Deadwood Pass was just to the left of it. He wondered how much longer he would be able to keep his herd together, for much of the time it was difficult even to see the cattle.

His heart sank in despair. What if he failed and they were all lost in the storm — he and Blackie, as well as the cattle? He recalled how, as a little boy, he would run to his mother when he was afraid, to bury his head in her lap. She would pat his head and say comforting things to him until his fears were gone. Now fear gripped him as never before. But his mother was far away. There was no comforting lap to run to, no reassuring word. In spite of himself he sobbed. But he must go on. He gulped back tears as he pushed the herd forward.

Soon they moved into Deadwood Pass, only three miles from the Bar-X Ranch and home.

Growing colder every minute, the boy became sleepy. In order to rouse himself from the stupor creeping over him, he started to shout. There was an added reason for his shouting, too. If his father had returned, he would start out to meet him. Again and again he shouted until his throat became rough and his voice hoarse. He couldn't keep that up much longer, he thought. He gave one last long hallooooooo—

Then came an answering shout — not an echo — his father's voice!

The boy gave a long sigh of relief as his father rode up.

"Where's Zeb?" he shouted in surprise.

"He couldn't go with me. His wife is sick."

"You went alone?"

"Yes, sir. I had to."

"Oh!" There was a short, tense silence. "It's all right now, Son. We'll soon have the cattle in."

Nat took over the herding and didn't speak again except to give directions. This was no time for talk. Snow was falling, the clouds were lifting, and the wind was lighter.

Soon the herd was safe in the corral, and Blackie had been cared for.

"Are all the cattle here, Father?" George asked anxiously.

"Almost all," his father replied. "I didn't count them, but if any are missing, they are not far away. We'll hunt for them in the morning."

Father and son went into the house.

"I heard you coming," Elta said. "Why, where's Zeb? I thought he'd stay for supper or at least come in to get warm."

"Zeb didn't go, Mother. Mandy's hurt," George replied.

"George! You went alone!" Elta's eyes were filled with fear for what might have happened. "If I'd known that, I'd have followed you up on the range."

"It's all right now, Mother. There's nothing to worry about." George tried to laugh, but his voice was shaky.

"George is right, Elta," Nat said gently.

"You needn't worry about this son of ours. He has the sense and the courage of a man, even if he hasn't the years of a man." He laid a kind hand on the boy's shoulder.

George looked from one to the other, unable to speak. He looked about the cozy, friendly kitchen. His throat was so tight he could scarcely breathe. He felt he was going to cry. But his father had just said he had the strength and courage of a man.

Swallowing hard, George went over to the basin in the corner to wash his hands. His father and mother understood why he didn't speak.

— *J. A. Rickard*

Things to Do

1. Why was a blizzard greatly feared by ranchers long ago? How are cattle fed and protected now when blizzards come?

2. Choose members of your class to read parts of the story aloud. The list of scenes below may help you.
   a. George tells his mother good-by.
   b. He decides to go alone for the herd.
   c. Alone on the range at night.
   d. The blizzard
   e. Driving the herd home
   f. Meeting his father
   g. Home again

3. Make a list of words that describe George's feelings during the blizzard, and also when he heard his father's voice.

Outdoor World

The Banner, the Bird and Bush

(A play for a holiday or for any time. If the play is given other than on July 4, substitute correct date.)

Characters

MR. PARKER

MRS. PARKER

PATSY, *their nine-year-old daughter.*

JIMMY, *their eleven-year-old son, who is a Boy Scout.*

TIME: *The morning of July the Fourth.*

SETTING: *The Parker living room and dining room combined, with a rear exit to the outside and another exit to the kitchen. Mrs. Parker sweeping and cleaning the dining end of the room. Mr. Parker standing and fastening the suspenders of his overalls. Patsy helping her mother. Jimmy on the floor reading the morning paper.*

MR. PARKER: The Fourth of July! I'm glad it's a holiday, so I can work at home instead of going to the office. The backyard hedge needs trimming badly. It's more than a foot too tall already.

MRS. PARKER: Watch for wasp nests, or you may get stung. I think there's a sparrow's nest in it too.

MR. PARKER: I'll knock them all down. Wasps and sparrows are both pests. One's about as bad as the other.

MRS. PARKER: Before you go, maybe you should give Patsy her present.

MR. PARKER: That's right. I completely forgot— I was so anxious to get to work. (*He exits, then returns with a small flag of the United States.*)

PATSY: (*Receiving it, excited*) — A flag! and for me? How nice! But where shall I put it?

MR. PARKER: Put it in your bedroom, over your bed, and sleep under it. And remember, my daughter, that this flag protects all who are under it.

PATSY: Thank you for the nice gift, but (*hesitating*) — er — Daddy — don't you think English sparrows are pretty nice little birds?

MR. PARKER: Nice! They bring fleas and mites! They run off other birds! They're a con-

founded nuisance, I say. I wish we didn't
have any on the place. (*Exit mumbling*).

PATSY: (*Goes over to where Jimmy is reading
on the floor*). Oh Jimmy! What can we do?

JIMMY: (*Looking up from paper*). Huh? Do?
What do you mean?

PATSY: Daddy's gone out to clip the whole hedge.

JIMMY: Sure. I heard him say that. It needs
it, doesn't it?

PATSY: But Mother Sparrow has a nest in that

tall hedge bush yonder at the corner (*pointing*). I looked in it yesterday. It had one little egg and one tiny, naked bird in it. He opened his mouth at me, and I put in a worm. There may be *two* birds by now (*grows more excited as she talks*). And Daddy's going to cut them all down (*almost crying*).

JIMMY: Gee! I didn't know all that. We've got to do something. Let's tell him about the nest.

PATSY: I started to just now, but you heard what he said. He — he — called them a con — confounded nuisance. He — he — wished we didn't have any English sparrows on the place! (*Sobs a little and dabs at eyes with a handkerchief*).

JIMMY: (*Rising to his feet*). Let's phone Uncle Bill's folks and ask them to come over right quick. They would get here before he reached the nest, maybe, and he would quit work.

PATSY: But he would finish later. And Uncle Bill's folks aren't at home. I heard them say yesterday they wouldn't be there today.

JIMMY: Let's ask Mother. Maybe she can think of something.

MRS. PARKER: (*Who has come into the room earlier and has been listening*). I heard what you said, although I did not mean to eaves-drop. I'm sure there must be some way to save Mother Sparrow's home without mentioning the matter to Daddy. Maybe you could cut off the whole limb, nest and all, and move it to some other place.

PATSY: I wouldn't know where to move it.

JIMMY: That wouldn't do anyhow, Mother, I'm afraid, for some birds quit their nests when people handle them.

MRS. PARKER: Well, children, I don't know what else to tell you to do. Your father is a good man, though, and I'm sure he would do right if he saw what was right. Now I have to watch that cake to take it out of the oven when it is done.

PATSY: (*Jumping up, excited*). I have it! (*Grabs the flag and starts toward the rear exit*).

JIMMY: Where are you going?

PATSY: I'm going to put this flag up above Mother Sparrow's nest. Here, let me have that string for tying it. (*Jimmy hands her the string, and she starts out again, this time disappearing from view through the rear exit*).

JIMMY: (*To himself, as he looks out*). My, but that was sudden! And she's already there! Now she has the flag tied up! And Daddy's not far away! He'll be there in a few minutes at the rate he's going! Here she comes, running back!

PATSY: (*Breathing hard as she enters*). I did it! And I don't think Daddy saw me. He was on the other side of the hedge, and I hurried.

JIMMY: Was Mother Sparrow on her nest?

PATSY: Yes, and she fussed at me when I disturbed her. I tried to tell her what I was doing, but I don't think she understood.

JIMMY: She flew back to the nest after you left — I saw her do it.

PATSY: Oh, but what will Daddy do? I wish I knew!

JIMMY: (*Looking out*). We ought to know soon, for he's almost there now.

PATSY: Oh, I can't stand to watch! I'm going to help Mother. You tell me what happens. (*Exit to kitchen*).

JIMMY: (*Looking again*). He has reached it! He has seen it! He has started to the house! I must go tell her! (*Exit, calling "Patsy! Patsy!"*).

MR. PARKER: (*Enters, carrying flag on a piece of green twig. Enter also Patsy and Jimmy, followed by Mrs. Parker*). You sly rascals. (*smiling*). That was a bright idea if I ever heard of one.

PATSY: (*Running to her father*). Daddy! You didn't, did you?

MR. PARKER: How could I? How could *anyone* hurt anything with our flag flying over it? (*Puts his arms around her*).

PATSY: But, Daddy, I just took you at your word. You said that flag protected all who were under it, and I thought that meant birds as well as people.

MR. PARKER: So it does, it seems.

JIMMY: Say, Daddy, you would make a good Boy Scout. You've done your daily good turn. Do you know the salute to the flag?

MR. PARKER: Maybe I could stumble through it. And if you will lead it, we will all say it. Come on now, Patsy and Mother. (*They gather in a group and face the audience, at attention*).

JIMMY: (*To audience*). Maybe the audience would like to join us in the salute to the flag.

EVERYONE: I pledge allegiance to the flag of the United States of America and to the republic for which it stands; one nation under God, indivisible, with liberty and justice for all.

Curtain:

— *J. A. Rickard*

Things to Do

1. Recently a teacher was shocked to discover that only a few of her children knew why the Fourth of July is a holiday in our country. Do you know?
2. Why is this play an appropriate one for the Fourth of July?
3. What is the meaning of the title? How was this proved in the play?
4. Choose characters, and read the play aloud.
5. At the end of the play, sing the *Star Spangled Banner*.
6. A group of younger children might enjoy hearing your class read the play. What props and costumes would be needed?

Donkey for Rent

Papá Martínez looked over the top of his paper as his ten-year-old son came in late for breakfast.

"Juan, you must do something about that donkey," he said in severe tones.

Juan pushed back his thick black hair, rubbed his eyes, and asked, "Why, Papá? What has he done now?"

"He's broken loose again and eaten up neighbor García's carrots. That's the third complaint I've had from neighbors. Then — yesterday I had to pay a two-dollar feed bill on him."

Juan's face was anxious now. "But Papá, he's lots of fun. I've always wanted pets, and he's the best one I've ever had. I'll fix the gate so he can't break out. I'll make some money to pay his feed, too, if you'll only let me keep him."

Mamá Martínez came to her son's aid. "Give the boy a chance," she pleaded. "Maybe he can do something about it."

"Oh, well," said Papá Martínez, feeling sorry, "I don't want to be called cruel. I'll give you a month. Let's see. This is July 25. The feed bill is now four dollars, and another sack of corn will have to be bought soon. See if you can earn that money. And remember, keep him out of mischief." A minute later Señor Martínez went to work.

Juan walked slowly to the neat, white shed behind the house. There, in a ten-foot stall that had once belonged to Rosita, the cow, stood Pepito. The donkey shook his big head and heehawed a welcome to his young master.

"You little pest," Juan scolded, as he stroked Pepito's velvety gray nose. "Why don't you stay out of mischief? And why do you eat so much? You are getting us both into trouble."

Pepito flapped his long ears and went on eating corn.

Juan tied a rope around the donkey's neck,

put a loop over his nose, and went out to find Octavio and Pablo. They were playing ball in a vacant lot behind Pablo's house. Juan told them what his papá had said.

"It's not fair," cried Octavio. "I'm the youngest of the three, and I paid two dollars on him. You and Pablo paid only one dollar each."

"Age doesn't count," answered Pablo in a voice that was changing to the voice of a man. "Anyhow, I furnished the harness and cart for him. You were to take care of him, Juan."

"I know I was," Juan admitted. "But I've kept him three months, and he has eaten two sacks of corn and bothered all the neighbors. Papá says I must do something about it in a month."

"Maybe we could put the gate latch where Pepito can not reach it," declared Pablo. "Let's try it."

Pablo fetched a hammer. Octavio brought a screwdriver. He was too small to use it very well, but Juan helped him. In thirty minutes they had put the latch on the outside of the stall, where Pepito's teeth could not reach it.

While they were working, Juan saw the long lariat that had been used to stake the cow. It gave him an idea.

"Pepito could not slip that off, for it fastens with a snap," he said, so he picked it up

and snapped it around the donkey's neck. They found that it was a good fit.

"Hurrah!" cried Octavio, his little brown face lighting with pleasure. "Now we have solved our problem. He'll not get loose when we stake him."

"No," Juan reminded him. "We haven't found a way yet to earn money for Pepito's feed."

"That's so. I forgot. What can we do?" asked Octavio, as he looked at his older friends.

"If we could only think of some way to let

him earn his own money," suggested Pablo.

Juan let out a whoop. "I have it! We'll put an ad in the paper and say he is for rent! Folks make money renting houses and other things."

Soon the three boys were trying to think of the right words for their ad. Juan, who could write best, was using pencil and paper, while Pablo offered suggestions and little Octavio helped. By putting together their savings, they counted fifty cents.

"That will do for having it printed three times," announced Juan, whose papá worked in the newspaper plant.

Two days later the readers of the *Kingsville News* saw in the classified columns an item which read:

DONKEY FOR RENT. Gentle to ride. Will pull anything. Likes children. Fifty cents and board per day, delivered. Phone 558, or see Juan Martínez, 801 Huisache Street.

Late in the afternoon, one month later, Juan and Octavio were sitting on the front door step of Juan's home.

"Let's see," figured Octavio, as he screwed up his mouth and for a second time counted the money in his hand. "I took him four Tuesdays to be mascot for that softball team at their games."

"And the Jones children have rented him

four times, and the Wilson children twice," added Juan. "That makes five dollars in all. We need six."

"The Chamber of Commerce has him in the parade today, and Pablo is riding him," declared Octavio. "But that's only fifty cents. We still won't have enough. It's a shame!" He clinched his little fist as he said it, and tears came into his eyes.

"Never mind," Juan said, putting an arm around the little boy's shoulder. "It'll come out all right."

Just then they heard a shout. Pepito was approaching at a fast gallop. Pablo was bouncing up and down on his back.

"We won the prize! We won the prize!" he yelled, jumping off the donkey. He pointed proudly to a blue ribbon tied on Pepito's bridle.

"What prize? Tell us about it!" the two other boys asked at once, as Pablo turned a cartwheel on the lawn.

"Five dollars! The judges said Pepito was the cutest thing in the parade, and they gave him first prize!"

Papá Martínez came in from work just then, and the boys crowded around him, all of them talking at once. Raising his hand to quiet them, he said, "Well, well, I guess Pepito has earned his keep, after all."

Then, with a twinkle in his eyes he asked, "Say, is he for sale?"

"No sir, just for rent," answered Juan.

— *J. A. Rickard*

Things to Do

1. The boys in this story solved a problem by "using their heads." Have you ever tried to work out plans for earning money to buy something that you wanted very much? Tell the class about your money-making idea.

2. Make a list of the Spanish names and words in the story. Beside each word, write its meaning in English.

The Shoe Gobbler

Johnny was having great fun in the country. Summer vacation time had finally arrived. As he lay in bed, he wondered what Grandfather would show him this morning. Suddenly he jumped up, for he was afraid he was late for breakfast.

"That rooster will have to crow louder in the morning," said Grandmother fondly, as she poured melted butter and golden syrup over Johnny's waffle.

Grandfather rose from the table and took off his glasses. "It's the turkeys we need to watch," he said. "I think they've hidden a nest in the woods beyond the barn."

"Oh, may I find it?" asked Johnny eagerly.

"Yes," Grandfather said thoughtfully, "but maybe you should wait till feeding time — the grass is wet with dew now. Then — be sure to wear your shoes to protect your feet from grass burrs."

Johnny could hardly wait for the time. He hurried to the house and pulled on his shoes. "I'll be back soon," he promised Grandmother, as he ran toward the big red barn.

The turkeys were just starting toward the

woods. He crawled through the plank barn-lot fence and crept along after them. He wondered which one had the nest; so when one brown hen left the others, he decided to follow her.

She hurried until she reached the woods; then she stopped and stuck out her long neck this way and that. Johnny squatted down, trying to be very quiet, for he was afraid she had seen him.

Maybe she hadn't though, he decided, for soon she darted ahead. She went some distance into the woods. Johnny tiptoed after her. Finally, she stopped in a clump of bushes. Ah, surely there was her nest!

How he wished he could see it! Maybe he could if he was careful. Slipping from bush to bush, he crept closer and closer, until he was within five feet of her.

Just then he tripped and fell almost on top of the nest! The turkey gave a scared "prut! prut!" and darted away.

Johnny picked himself up and brushed off the dirt. He was sorry he had scared Mother Turkey, but he must see that nest, now that he was so near.

What he saw made him catch his breath, for there were eight tiny, downy, yellow turkeys and one egg. All of them were cheeping loudly as if they were scared. One little fellow still

had a piece of shell on his back.

"Don't be afraid. I won't hurt you," whispered Johnny softly, as he stroked the back of one downy baby.

A rumble of thunder made him look up. He saw that the sky was covered with clouds. He had been too busy to notice the weather.

He looked again at the little turkeys. They were helpless now. If it should rain they would drown. He must keep them dry and take them away.

But how could he carry them? There were too many for his hands or pockets. They would be soaked if he put them in his hat. Since it was looking more like rain every minute, he had to do something quickly.

He could think of only one way to protect them. He pulled off his shoes, put the little turkeys into them, and covered them with his hat. Then he hurried toward the house.

The rain caught him at the edge of the

woods, and my, how it did rain! It came down in sheets instead of drops. He stopped under a tree, but soon he was wet to the skin. He hugged the shoes in his arms, keeping the hat down over them. Whatever else happened, the babies must be protected from the downpour.

Although he thought it would never stop raining, it did — finally. He was cold and shaking, but when he peeped under the hat and saw the little turkeys still dry, he felt better.

Without hat or shoes, he started across the pasture. The grass burrs stuck in his feet, but he pulled them out and kept on going. He just had to go on, even if his feet did hurt.

He surely was glad when he saw Grandfather taking long steps across the pasture. Grandfather's face had an anxious look, but he tried to joke about it.

"Well, well, you've brought a rain," he said. "We'll send you out again when it is too dry."

Then he noticed the hat and shoes which Johnny was holding so carefully. "Say, you did want to get wet. Why didn't you pull off the rest of your clothes?"

Johnny was not afraid now. He even smiled and looked mysterious. "It's a present for Grandmother," he explained. "You'll be surprised when you see it."

"Fine! Let's carry it to her. But you'll take a cold in those wet clothes," Grandfather said, as he and Johnny hurried toward the house.

Grandmother had a fire burning. She hustled Johnny into dry clothes, while Grandfather made him a cup of hot tea. The boy didn't have time to talk.

Presently from the bundle in the corner near the fireplace there came a faint "cheep! cheep!"

"Dear me," exclaimed Grandmother, pulling down her glasses to look at the bundle. "What is that?"

"That's my present," cried Johnny. "Eight little turkeys!"

Grandmother lined a basket with a soft, warm blanket to hold them.

"Say — you can't count!" exclaimed Grandmother as she put in the last one. "There are nine!"

Johnny didn't know what to say, but Grandfather came to his rescue. "That last one hatched out in the shoe," he said. He will belong to Johnny. Mark him so we'll know him. By Christmas he will be a large turkey."

Johnny found his voice at last. "I guess we'll call him the shoe gobbler," he said happily.

— *J. A. Rickard*

Things to Do

1. This story would be enjoyed also by children in a
   lower grade. Prepare it to read aloud to a third
   or fourth grade group. Several persons may read
   parts of it.
2. Introduce your story by having someone give information about turkeys — how they build nests,
   the food they eat, and other habits.

Big Horns and the New Fence

Big Horns, Gray Fawn, and Bashful Doe actually lived on a ranch in western Texas. This story is true except, perhaps, that Big Horns spoke in antelope language which has been translated into English here.

The old pronghorn shook his head and pawed the ground, as he looked again at the wire fence which those cowboys were building.

He was no stranger to fences, but never before had he seen one like this. It was not made of long, straight wires, such as were around part of the big pasture where he lived. It was heavy and tall and was made of small squares. He and his mates could double up their legs and crawl between the wires of the old fence, or they could even jump over it; but they could do neither with this one.

The fence posts were already set, too, and all the wire but a short stretch had been stapled to them. The part that was not stapled was flat on the ground, but soon it would be up. It was enclosing the very place where he and his mates lived. And unless they could get over that six feet of wire lying flat on the ground, they were prisoners inside.

It was the middle of the day, and the cowboys had stopped work for awhile. Maybe Big Horns could do something. His curiosity, always keen, was now sharpened by the danger. One step at a time, smelling at every step, he moved closer to the fence. He stuck his nose against the cold steel of a square of wire.

He jumped back at the touch, ready to run if it should come to life. But it did not move.

It remained flat on the ground, its stiff wires stretched out between him and liberty.

He went back to where Gray Fawn and Bashful Doe were standing.

"Come on and look at it," he urged them. "It did not harm me, and I touched it."

"But I'm afraid," said Bashful Doe.

"So am I," said Gray Fawn. "It smells like people."

"But no people are near," he argued. "You can see that for yourselves."

Finally they did venture up close enough to touch the wire with their noses, but Bashful Doe smelled too hard. A small part of the wire moved. That was enough to send all three of them flying off in terror.

Big Horns stopped first. As the leader of that little herd, it was his duty to be brave. And if they remained free, they would have to jump over that wire on the ground. Nor was there much time left. Those cowboys would be back to finish that fence; then it would be too late to escape. But if he should jump over it, maybe his mates would follow.

He ran back to where they were huddled in a fearful little knot. Twice he circled around them.

"Come on. Follow me," he told them. Then he ran toward the fence as fast as he could

and leaped.

He jumped far enough to clear the fence on the ground, but he had risen three feet before reaching it. As he landed, he struck the far edge of the wire; his left hind foot caught in it, and he stumbled.

He was so scared that he trembled, but he had to get back to his friends. Even though he was free, they were not, for they had not followed him. He conquered his fears and jumped again. This time he cleared the fence by three feet and galloped back to them.

"Come on," he pleaded, "and do as I do." He made another run at the fence. Again he cleared it without touching a wire, but still they were afraid to jump. There was nothing for him to do but leap back to them.

This time as he circled them he shook his horns in a most threatening way. They held back, but Gray Fawn did follow him a short distance. Bashful Doe did not even move, and presently Gray Fawn went back to her. Big Horns had jumped again, but his jumping had been in vain.

He was growing desperate now. The cowboys had returned, and his sharp eyes could see them watching from a distant hill. Even as he watched, they began to stir about.

There was time for only one more jump. Big Horns circled his mates three times this trip. Then with lowered horns he dived at them. They fled before him, and he crowded them ever closer to the fence. After he had forced them halfway, he took the lead for the jump.

This time they followed, and after he leaped, they leaped. All three jumped over the wire to freedom.

Two of the cowboys cheered as the animals faded from sight across the prairie. The third one removed his hat and smiled.

"That was worth seeing," he said. "Antelopes are so timid that I didn't believe they would ever do it. I did want them in our new pasture, but I guess they've earned their liberty."

— *Mrs. T. F. Slay, as told to J. A. Rickard*

Things to Do

1. Why was Big Horns afraid of the new fence?
2. What made him overcome his fear of it?
3. How did he help his mates overcome their fear?
4. Why did the cowboys applaud the escape?
5. The story of Big Horns and the New Fence would make a good puppet show. The puppets may be the hand or stick kind. A pupil may tell or read the story as the puppets perform.
6. Become the pronghorn specialist in your room by finding out everything that you can about this fleetest of animals.
7. In your library, find out about the American antelope or pronghorn.

Frank and His Friend Mallie

Spring had come to the Lone Elm ranch, and Frank was idly watching some ducks, as they swam in the spring-fed pond a hundred yards east of the barns. His mother interrupted his thoughts.

"Would you like to help me set a hen?" she asked, her gray eyes proudly resting on her son's overgrown figure. "It's not quite as exciting as chasing cattle or going on a roundup, but maybe it would interest an eleven-year-old boy."

"I'd like it," he replied, "and maybe we ought to put our brand on the eggs to keep the chickens from straying."

"Let's wait till they are hatched," she said, smiling as she led the way toward the barns.

He followed her into the henhouse near the other buildings. She stopped in front of a nest containing a clucking hen and gently laid an apron full of eggs on the straw-covered ground. Then, carefully, two at a time, she slipped them under the hen. Frank counted them; there were fifteen, and three had green marks.

"Why, those are duck eggs!" he exclaimed. "I can tell by their shape and coloring. Why are you putting them under the hen? And what do those marks mean?"

"One question at a time, please. I believe that a hen makes a better mother than a duck. And the ones you see marked are wild duck eggs. My nearest neighbor at the T-Bar ranch gave them to me yesterday."

Frank thought this nothing unusual, even though the "nearest neighbor" was five miles away. He said, "Maybe I had better help old mother hen raise these ducks. I'm sure she'll need help."

"Very well, if you want to. But *you* may be needing it before long."

And several times in later months Frank remembered his mother's words. He started off well enough. Early each morning and late each afternoon he gave Mother Hen something to eat. And to be sure that things were going along as they should, he often raised her high enough off the nest to look at the warm eggs under her. Always he took a second look at the three eggs with the green marks.

She did not seem to object to this. Sometimes she did fuss a little, in a mild clucking way; but always she settled down on her nest again, and moved the eggs about with her body.

The boy understood that this was her way of preventing the eggs from becoming one-sided, and allowing them to hatch properly. He was pretty sure she was not objecting to his "peeping ways." He wondered how she learned that egg turning trick; he guessed she just knew it from the first.

In about three weeks little holes began to appear in the eggs, through which he could see tiny bills. Then the shells cracked open, and down-covered babies looked out at Frank from under the edge of their mother's wings when he raised the mother hen for a look. She was clucking more than ever now, and there was a new sound to her clucks, he thought; a proud sound, as if she were trying to say, "Look! See my babies!"

In one way Frank was disappointed; only twelve of the eggs hatched. And two of those that did not hatch were marked green. He resolved then that he and the mother hen would raise that one wild duck or know the reason why.

And he wasn't going to make her do all the work; he began to help. Out of old lumber he built for them a pen that protected them from cold nights and spring rains. He also made a feed trough and a watering trough, into which they could get their heads but not their feet. They would have clean food to eat, he said to

himself, and that ought to make them healthy. Each night he shut them up carefully, and each morning he kept them indoors until the dew was gone.

So interested did he become in his new pets that he studied bulletins which told how to feed and care for them, and with his own hands he mixed their feed and gave it to them. Once he asked a neighbor who was going to El Paso to buy some medicine to prevent roup.

Frank had to admit that the mother hen was doing her part, but so far as she was concerned he could see that her ducklings were problem children. If raising them had not been such a serious problem with him, he would have laughed at some of her troubles. As it was, he had to smile now and then, for those ducklings just would not behave like baby chickens.

For one thing, they did not seem to know what their foster mother meant by her clucking. Sometimes, when she found something to eat, she clucked long and loud. Now and then they came to her, but most of the time they struck out for themselves and went where they pleased. Usually she had to go in a clucking trot to keep up with them.

But the worst part of Mother Hen's life came when her babies discovered the pond of water.

With delighted little quacks they plunged into it, and out into the very middle they swam. All the frantic mother could do was to stand at the edge of the pond and cluck, while they went on across.

Frank had to laugh a little that time, even if he was sorry for old Mother Hen. Thereafter, when he missed his pets, he knew where to find them — at the pond. And usually, their guardian was calling them in vain, while they paddled in the water or stuck their heads under and paid no attention to her.

Even so, the strange family grew and prospered. Before they were many weeks old Frank could tell that one of them had a green neck and head. His father told him that the newcomer was a mallard, so Frank named him Mallie.

Mallie learned his name rather quickly. All Frank had to do was to shout "Mallie! Mallie!" or cry out, "Quack! Quack!" The ducklings might be fifty yards away at the time, but here they would come waddling toward him, with Mallie in the lead.

Frank wondered why he could get them to come when Mother Hen could not. He guessed it was because he always fed them, or perhaps he called louder than did old Mother Hen. Or maybe he didn't try to keep them from going where they wanted to go, as she did. Indeed, she finally gave up and quit trying to be a mother to them. She weaned them, as Frank's mother put it. She went her way and let them go theirs.

By that time they were no longer ducklings — they were almost grown. Frank half dreaded the moment when Mallie would learn that he could fly. His father had already warned him that sooner or later he would learn, and maybe leave home. The boy did not want him to leave. He loved all the cows and horses that were on the ranch. At that time though, with the exception of his pony, Dixie, he guessed he loved Mallie most of all.

Sure enough, Mallie did learn what his wings were for. One day some thirsty horses dashed up to the edge of the pond, stopping quickly within a few feet of Mallie and his mates. Most of them quacked in fear and swam toward the middle of the pond in a hurry, but Mallie rose up and *flew!* And he did not stop until he was safely on the ground inside the barnyard.

After that he flew often, and once he went completely out of sight over the trees beyond the barn. Fearing that at this rate he would soon be gone for good, Frank clipped the ends of the feathers on one of Mallie's wings. The next time he tried to fly he went around in circles, and finally came to the ground with a thud that made him lie still. Full of regret,

Frank ran and picked him up in his arms. He patted Mallie's head, and said he was sorry, then promised that he would never clip any more feathers from his wings.

He kept that promise, even though he knew it meant that Mallie might fly away for good some day. But wild ducks did not come their way very often. And as summer turned to fall, then to winter, with Mallie still at home, Frank began to grow hopeful again. Maybe, after all, Mallie would stay at home with the tame ducks and not leave.

But somewhere from his wild ancestors Mallie had learned some tricks that tame ducks did not know. And he began to teach them to his mates. One of these tricks was to keep the pond from freezing over too hard for swimming. Frank had been wondering what his pets would do when the ice came. He had about decided to take an axe and keep a small hole cut out, in which they could at least get to the water.

But Mallie showed him a better way to solve that problem. With Frank watching, fascinated, from the land, Mallie flew around and around, flapping the tips of his wings in the water. The flying circles grew larger and larger, the duck's wings breaking the thin ice. On and on he flew until most of the pond was ice-free. Then, with a satisfied quack, he rested on the

water. When Frank clapped his hands and shouted, "hurrah!" Mallie flapped his wings happily and dipped his long green head and neck below the surface. He and his mates had a swimming place all winter.

The duck and the boy became fast friends. Mallie learned to reach his long neck high into the air to take corn from Frank's hand, and to stick his bill into the boy's coat pocket for grains of wheat which were always there — on purpose. With his funny waddling pace he followed Frank up to the back door of the ranch house, and a few times he even went into the kitchen. He was a full grown drake by now, and was proud of his fine appearance. His feathers were greener than ever, and with his bill he smoothed them until every one lay perfectly in place.

But spring came, and Mallie grew restless. His quacks were becoming a little more frequent, and his air trips longer and closer together. Frank knew that some day a flock of Mallie's wild kinsfolk would stop at the little pond on their way north, and he found himself watching it anxiously.

They did come one night — six of them. Frank, taking his usual early morning look, saw them on the water with Mallie and his mates. He started to go down to the pond, then an idea came to him. Perhaps the newcomers would become frightened at the sight of him more quickly than Mallie would. If they should, they might fly up and be out of sight before his pet could make up his mind what to do.

Slowly and cautiously he slipped down toward the pond, then he stopped. He couldn't do it. He guessed ducks had the same right as people to live the kind of lives they wanted to live. No, Mallie would have to decide for himself whether to go or stay. He turned his back on the pond, and swallowed to choke back the tight feeling in his throat. Slowly he turned and walked back to the house. When old Tong, the big bull dog, started toward the pond, Frank called him back, patted his head, and took him into the house.

But he was so restless that he couldn't stay in the house himself. He was glad when his father called and told him to ride out to the west pasture and drive up a cow and a newly born calf.

He was not surprised when his mother, at the dinner table, said, "Mallie is gone. He flew off with those wild ducks that came to the pond last night."

Frank was having so much trouble cutting up a piece of steak that his father kindly answered for him.

"It's the way of all wild things, Son. It had to be."

"Yes sir," said Frank. He couldn't have said more if he had wanted to.

He tried to be interested in the other ducks, and of course there was Dixie. School started again too, and he was kept busy riding back and forth ten miles each day.

But he kept going back to the pond. He did not dare put into words the reason why he was going back, but somewhere back in his mind was a faint hope. The wild things were flying again — going south this time. Maybe Mallie —

One crisp evening he was startled by the swish of wings and the sudden dip of flying bodies to the pond. The boy, standing thirty feet away, froze in his tracks. Then he called out softly, "Mallie! Mallie! Quack! Quack!"

One of the forms on the water separated itself from the rest of the group and waddled up the bank toward him. His old friend had come back for a visit!

— *J. A. Rickard*

Things to Do

1. How did Frank become interested in raising ducks?
2. What troubles did Mother Hen have with her strange children?
3. How did Frank's pet get his name?
4. How did Mallie keep the pond from freezing over?
5. Why did the pet leave home?
6. Under what conditions did he return?
7. Plan a movie of this story by illustrating each scene in it. Your first illustration would show Frank and his mother setting the hen. Decide upon the other scenes that you would need.
8. Record the parts of the story with a tape recorder as you or your classmates read the parts aloud. Put the pictures and recordings together to make a movie or TV show! Invite another class to share your show.

Folk Tales
The Coo Bird

A Mexican Folk Tale

In the long, long ago the Great Creator made the world. It seemed so dreary and solemn that he wanted to make everything more cheerful. One day he decided to make birds. He made all sizes of birds from the smallest wren to the largest eagle. But something was still lacking. They looked droopy and sad and did not sing very much.

"I know what is the trouble," He said. "They need bright and beautiful clothing. I will make some especially for them."

He then made many, many feathers, large and small. These he gave out to the birds, and soon they were making the world pleasant and happy with their songs.

But He ran out of feathers a short while before every bird was supplied. He thought he had clothed them all, but one little bird called the coo bird remained naked. The Creator had overlooked it and gone back to His sky home.

The coo bird looked so ugly that the other birds were either ashamed of him, or sorry for him. They had a meeting to see what should be done.

"Each of us could give him a single feather," said the wise old owl. "We would not miss one tiny feather, and he would be well covered."

"I object," replied the peafowl, looking at his own handsome feathers, "for then he would be so pretty that he would be too proud to live with us."

Some of the other birds agreed with the peafowl, but the owl argued with them. The chaparral cock, or road runner, and two or three other birds, agreed with the owl.

Finally, the friends of the coo bird said, "If you will adopt our plan, we will guarantee the good conduct of our newly feathered friend."

That promise caused the other birds to accept the proposal. Each bird then gave a single feather until the little coo bird was fully covered. In fact, no other bird in the whole world was so grandly clothed as he. When he saw his image in the water where he went to drink, he became vain indeed.

He looked at himself a minute and said, "Why, I am the most beautiful bird of all the birds. None of them, not even the peacock, is so grandly dressed as I."

He drank again and looked at himself once more. "Why, I am too beautiful to be found in the company of these uglier birds," he decided. "I'll not associate with them any longer."

So saying, he flew into the sky and did not return.

The other birds were now angry with the owl. They were so angry that they scolded him and pecked him and made life miserable for him. To escape, he flew away to the side of a hill. There he found a small hole in which he hid, coming out only at night.

The road runner went to look for him, and when he found him, he carried him some lizard food to eat. They talked over the matter fully and decided to look for the missing coo bird. A few other bird friends joined them, and so began a long search.

They are still looking. At night the owl flies from tree to tree and calls, "Coo! coo! coo!" In the daytime the road runner hops and runs from bush to bush and calls "Coo root! Coo root!" Another bird friend that stays in clocks comes out every hour and calls, "Coo, coo! Coo, coo!"

But so far they have not found him.

— *J. A. Rickard*

Things to Do

1. When primitive people did not understand the cause of anything—a fact or an action—they created a reason for it. Read this story aloud and discuss what the Mexicans were trying to explain.
2. Can you tell similar folk tales, or would you like to try writing them? How do you think primitive people would have tried to explain an automobile, an airplane or an atomic explosion? Would this make a good subject for your story?

The Cunning Coyote

This is an Indian folk tale of the Southwest. It is well known to the Mexicans. In this story, as in many other Mexican tales, "El Coyote" is the most cunning animal.

A long, long time ago, when the world was young, a great quarrel arose among the animals. They argued long about who was the strongest.

"I am the strongest!" roared the lion.

"I am the strongest!" growled the bear.

"I am the strongest!" barked the wolf.

Many other animals squeaked, squawked, grunted, squealed, or meowed—each one claiming that he was the strongest of all.

The quarrel became so serious that some of the animals were ready to fight each other. Indeed, it looked as if there would be a regular animal war, with every animal fighting every other animal.

At length the Great Spirit took a hand in the matter.

"Now, now, this will never do," He said to his snarling subjects, "for if you get into a war, most of you will be killed."

They stopped their noise making; for when the Great Spirit spoke, everyone listened.

"Then, you decide the question for us," spoke
up one of the animals.

All the others said in one voice, "Yes, you
decide who is the strongest among us."

Now, the Great Spirit had not wanted this
responsibility, but finally He replied, "Very well.
I will consider the matter and send out my messengers tomorrow with my decision."

He thought long and hard. He talked with

his advisers. Early the next day His eagle messengers flew out to all parts of the world with loud speakers in their bills.

"Hear ye! Hear ye!" they told the world. "Two weeks from today His Majesty, the Great Spirit, will judge all the animals of the earth. Let every animal meet in the huge forest in front of the royal palace. He will rank each according to his strength. To the strongest He will give the longest and strongest bow and arrow. To the weakest He will give the shortest bow and arrow. To every animal He will give according to his strength. Hear ye! Hear ye! Be there without fail!"

At once there was such a moving about on the earth as was never seen before. On foot, through trees, by water, and in every other way that animals traveled, they came. Long before the day appointed to judge, the royal forest was filled with animals of every kind.

On the day before the bows and arrows were to be handed out, the animals went to bed early. The Great Spirit's plan was to begin handing out bows and arrows at sunrise. Each animal wanted to be on hand. If he were not present when his name was called, he would not get his bow and arrow.

All of them went to sleep but the coyote. He stayed awake on purpose. After dark, when the

other animals were snoring peacefully, he slipped
out without waking anyone.

"Maybe those bows and arrows are already
laid out. If they are, maybe I can get one first
of all," he said to himself.

During most of the night he looked, but
nothing could he find. If the Great Spirit had
already chosen the bows and arrows, He had
them hid in a safe place. Tired and sleepy, the

coyote slipped back to his camp a short while before daylight.

"I will just stay awake the rest of the time," he told himself, as he lay down at the edge of the woods. "Maybe if I am near the head of the line, I will get a long bow and arrow anyhow."

He lay down to wait, but his eyes became heavy. He scratched himself, and bit his paw, and chewed his tongue to stay awake. In spite of all he could do, his eyes went shut. Suddenly he was sound asleep.

He slept, and slept, and slept. When he awoke the sun was high, and everything about him was still and quiet. Not an animal was in sight.

He jumped up to look about him, but no moving thing could he see. In alarm, he followed the trail the other animals had taken, and soon he found the place where the bows and arrows had been.

One look told him that he was too late. All the long bows and arrows had been given to the other animals. Only one short pair was left for him—the shortest and weakest of all.

Poor coyote! He cried as if his heart would break. Finally, the Great Spirit became sorry for him.

"You can never be the strongest animal," He told the coyote, "but you can be the most cunning one'. From now on you will have twice as much cunning as any other animal in the world."

And so it is. Other animals are stronger than the coyote, but none so cunning.

— *J. A. Rickard*

Things to Do

1. This story could be illustrated in the way that comic strips are made. Make a "strip" of it. Use the strip for telling the story or use it in a class newspaper.
2. What is the meaning of the phrase, "according to his strength?" Can you say the same thing in another way?

Temo and the Emperor

A long time ago, before the white men came to America, the Aztec Indians had a great kingdom in Mexico. One of their great rulers was Nezahualcoyotl. That name is too difficult for most people to pronounce, but it means, "fasting coyote."

This emperor liked to hunt, so he had a large forest set aside for wild animals. He would not allow other people to go into that forest.

The emperor liked to go about among his people in disguise. Often he dressed as a peasant and talked to real peasants to learn how they lived. Not knowing who he was, the people would tell him things they would have been afraid to say if they had known he was their emperor.

On one occasion the disguised emperor was walking near the royal forest, when he met a little peasant boy named Temo. The boy was gathering sticks so that his family could have a fire to cook their meal into tortillas.

"My son," said the disguised emperor, "that wood you are gathering is hardly worth taking home. Why don't you go into yonder forest to gather sticks? That place contains plenty of good dry wood."

"But the forest belongs to our emperor," replied Temo. "He would put me to death if I went there."

"But he would not know it," replied the boy's companion. "No one will know it but me, and I will not tell anybody."

"You are a traitor or a spy," cried Temo angrily. "I will not listen to you."

"But isn't the wood going to waste? Your emperor must be a harsh man not to let you use it."

"He is a harsh man," agreed Temo. "He denies to his people what God meant for them to have. But should I do wrong because the emperor is harsh? No, my friend, I will not go into yonder forest." With these final words Temo marched away, carrying his little bundle of sticks with him.

Soon afterward a messenger from the emperor called at the humble home of Temo and his parents, commanding them to go to the royal palace. They went, full of fear and wondering if they had violated some law.

When the peasants saw Nezahualcoyotl, he was sitting on a grand throne, wearing jewels and dressed in fine robes; but Temo recognized him at once.

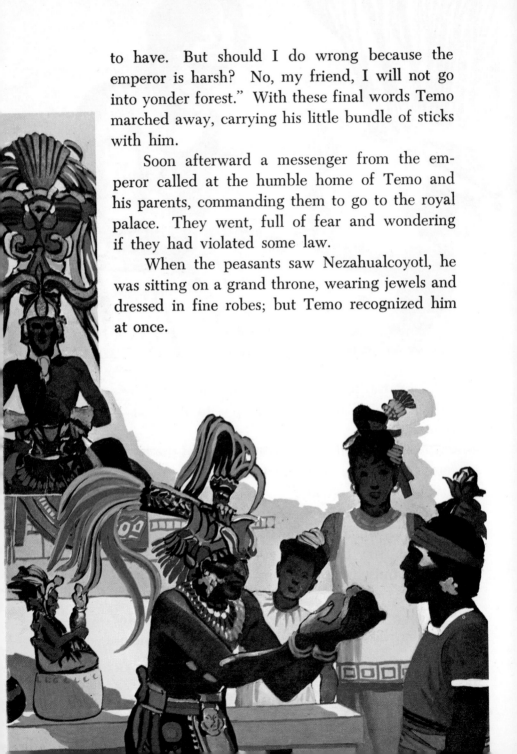

"Why, you are the man I met in the forest," he said, "and you told me to steal the emperor's wood."

"You are right, my child," answered the emperor, "but you did not steal the wood. Your parents have reared you well and taught you to be a good citizen. For that they shall be rewarded."

Thereupon the emperor had his attendants bring a large bag full of gold. This reward was given to Temo's father and mother. Best of all, the emperor himself went back with them to their humble peasant home and ate tortillas with Temo and his family.

After that, so the story goes, people were allowed to gather wood in the royal forest, if they did not use standing timber or kill any of the animals.

— *J. A. Rickard*

Things to Do

1. Dramatize this story in two scenes:
    a. Temo meets the emperor in the forest.
    b. Temo and his parents are summoned to the palace.
2. Discuss the characters needed for each scene.
3. Let each character make his dialogue as the dramatization is given; do not write it. Try to improve the dialogue in the story by creating your own.

The Legend of the Bluebonnet

Everybody who knows much about Texas is aware that the bluebonnet is the state flower. Surely no one who has seen it growing in masses by the roadside or in a nearby pasture in the spring has ever forgotten the sight. The bonnet-shaped blossoms with touches of white in their centers, like the ribbons for bonnets, sometimes grow so thickly above their dark green leaves that one wonders how the ground has space enough for them.

Old-timers used to call the plant "buffalo clover," but others, especially Latin Americans, said that the white tip of the flower resembled the tail of a cotton-tail rabbit. Certainly the strange wild sweetness of the bluebonnet can be seen and smelled but not described.

There is an old Indian legend which the Comanches and Cherokees knew and told. Much like some Aztec stories, it begins by saying that once, long ago, a great flood came to the land. The flood was followed by a disastrous drouth. Then winter — with its cold wind — the worst the Indians had ever known, descended without warning.

The cold weather extended far to the south where usually it was warm. So severe was it that the wild animals died or moved away, leaving the Indians without food. To add to these troubles, a deadly disease struck them, killing not only their old and young, but some of their healthiest men and strongest warriors. Nothing seemed to lighten their troubles. They prayed, fasted, and danced, but still they suffered.

At last the Great Spirit spoke to the wise men of the tribe. He told them He was angry. To make Him happy again, He commanded a burnt offering: the tribe's most valuable possession. It must be burned completely, said the Great Spirit, its ashes scattered to the four winds.

Around a solemn council fire, the elders of the tribe made known the words of the Great Spirit. There was much talk, yet no one seemed to know what their most precious possession was.

At this council fire was one silent observer, a little Indian girl. As she listened, she hugged to her bosom a small doll made of white fawn skin, its long braids of horsehair. Stuffed with

cotton and sewed with a rawhide string, it wore
a headdress of bird feathers like the warriors'.
With red berry juice the doll's eyes and other
features had been painted.

The child knew at once what the Great
Spirit wanted — what else but her doll? Certainly there was nothing that she loved so much. Her
duty was plain; she knew what she must do to
save the tribe. With heavy heart, she walked
away from the council fire.

It was night before she finally gained her
own consent to do her duty. Hugging her
precious doll, she slipped from her tepee into

the darkness. Far, far out — to a lonely spot she went. There with dry sticks she made a tiny fire. As soon as it burned brightly, she laid her offering on it, turning as the flames consumed her doll. After the fire died down, she scraped the ashes on to a flat board and scattered them in every direction.

Morning came before she had courage enough to tell her mother. Mother and daughter went to the scene of the burning. They found no ashes. Flowers, blue as the feathers of the jay that squawked and cried over the tepee, covered the spot.

The woman and child returned to tell the chieftain their tale. Immediately he called the tribe together. "Now we shall have rain and food and be freed of disease," he told them. "The command of the Great Spirit has been obeyed. The evils from which we are suffering will end."

Soon there was rain. The crops grew, the animals returned, and the birds sang again.

The Indians remembered their little friend. They changed her name to one which means, "She who dearly loves her people."

— *J. A. Rickard*

Things to Do

1. The Indians must have looked at the acres of bluebonnets in April and wondered "how the earth could hold so many." Probably because the Indians wondered, they made up a story to explain why the bluebonnets grow in the Southwest. What was the explanation?
2. Try to make up other "why" stories about the bluebonnets and share them with your classmates.

Weaving Time in Texas

It's weaving time in Texas,
They're weaving carpets there;
They're mixing in the greensward
A million colors rare.

There are miles and miles of carpet,
Spread out for dancing feet,
That touch the far horizon
Where sky and flowers meet.

It's weaving time in Texas,
And spring's the mistress there,
Directing southern maidens
With dark and flowing hair,

To form the leaves and flowers
Into a bold design;
To weave the blues and scarlets
Into a pattern fine;

To 'broider in the redbird
With gorgeous butterflies,
Till all the Texas landscape
A paradise defies.

— *William Dyer Moore*

The Rabbit and the Coyote

Joel Chandler Harris, or Uncle Remus, gave us Br'er Rabbit, whom we have seen laugh at the fox when he landed in the briar-patch—exactly where every rabbit feels at home! Br'er Rabbit has always been more cunning than his enemies, merely because he "uses his head." The Mexicans have folk tales that remind us of our Uncle Remus stories. A coyote is always the clever animal in their tales. However, he is always outwitted by the rabbit. Read these stories and compare them with one of the adventures of Br'er Rabbit by Uncle Remus.

In the Garden

One day the rabbit hopped into the farmer's garden. The farmer's wife came along and saw him. Then she shut the gate. The garden fence was so high that he could not jump it, and the wires were so close together that he could not crawl through.

Around and around the garden went he, with Mrs. Farmer in close pursuit but unable to catch him. Finally he saw a door and scurried through it, only to find that he was in a gallinero (gä yē nä′ rō) or henhouse that joined

the garden. He was trapped!

"Aha! I'll get you now," cried Mrs. Farmer.

But she was at home all alone, and she could not catch the rabbit without help. At length she thought of a way.

"I'll go to the house, heat some water, and scald off some of that fine fur. Then I'll bet you will wish you had stayed out of our garden," said she to herself as she shut the henhouse door.

Poor rabbit! He was in a terrible plight. To make matters worse, from the woods nearby came a coyote who jumped the garden fence and stood a minute eyeing the rabbit and wishing he had one of the chickens in the henhouse.

Finally he spoke. "Well, well, my fine friend, you seem to be in trouble."

"Oh, I don't know. It depends on what you call trouble," replied the rabbit. "They treat me wonderfully well and give me all that I can eat. But I don't like what they give me."

"What do you mean?" asked the coyote. "Why don't you eat some of those chickens?" His mouth watered as he said it.

"That's just it. It's chicken, chicken, chicken, three times a day. I have eaten so much chicken that I don't think I can ever look at a piece again. Now, if I only had some of those good carrots and peas out in that garden, I'd be satisfied."

"I'll tell you what. I will change places with you, for I like chickens," said the coyote.

That was just what the rabbit wanted. In no time the two had exchanged places. Soon the rabbit was eating carrots; the coyote was devouring a chicken. Hurriedly the farmer's wife returned with a bucket full of scalding water. She left the garden gate open, and rushed on to the henhouse. Seizing the opportunity, the rabbit dashed out of the gate. In a little while he heard the coyote howl.

"It is better to be wise than strong," the rabbit said as he hurried toward home.

At the Stream

Although he had been scalded badly, the old coyote finally escaped from the henhouse. He was angry with the rabbit and determined to catch him as soon as possible.

A few days later, while the coyote was out hunting, he came upon the rabbit close to a deep, broad stream. He was very near before the rabbit saw him. He knew he would be caught, if he ran toward the coyote; he also knew the coyote would outswim him and catch him, if he tried to swim across the stream.

The coyote sneered, "So I've got you at last. You might as well prepare to die."

"Wait a minute!" cried the rabbit." I have dropped a piece of cheese in the water, but I can't quite reach it. Let me hold your tail on the side of the bank here, so you can reach it."

The coyote liked cheese so well that he decided to bring the cheese up first, while he had help, and to eat the rabbit later. He went

down the edge of the steep bank, with the rabbit holding his tail. Just as they reached the water, the rabbit let go and ran away. By the time the coyote could climb out of the water, the rabbit was gone. This made the old coyote more furious than ever. He vowed that he would catch that rabbit some time and eat him, hide and all.

In the Woods

A few days later the coyote chanced upon
the rabbit under a tree where he was eating
some zapotes.[1] This time the rabbit was not
hemmed in or about to be caught, but he did
not want the coyote too close to him, because
he knew his foe could outrun him.

"Give me those zapotes, or I will catch
you and eat you," threatened the coyote.

[1]small tropical fruit

"Stay where you are! I will throw them to you," replied the rabbit.

He began throwing zapotes. He threw them so fast, in fact, that the coyote could not catch all of them. While he scrambled for one that he had missed, the rabbit reached over and picked a prickly pear. He threw it hard at the coyote just as the cunning one raised up. The thorny ball stuck right on his nose! "Mr. Rabbit" ran away, while the howling coyote frantically tried to pull out the prickly pear stickers.

Under the Pecan Tree

Soon afterward, the coyote again went out to hunt the rabbit. This time he discovered him under a pecan tree. Just as he was about to catch his prey, a pecan hit him on the head.

"Oh, what have you done to me?" cried the coyote as he howled with pain.

"My friend, it is hailing. You'd better come into my home, or you'll be killed!" exclaimed the rabbit.

He led his foe to a hole in the tree and courteously stepped back for his visitor to go in first. Though the hole was large enough for the rabbit, it was too small for the coyote. But so anxious was he to be inside that he tried

squeezing in anyway. Since only half of his
body went through, he became stuck and could
go no farther.

The rabbit ran away, laughing and saying,
"Mas vale maña que fuerza" (It is better to be
wise than strong).

— J. A. Rickard

Things to Do

1. What is a folk tale?
2. The characters in the folk tales used imagination to overcome fear and the unknown. Tell how the rabbit overcame fear in these four difficult situations:
   a. When he was caught in the henhouse.
   b. When the coyote caught the rabbit at a deep stream.
   c. When the rabbit was eating zapotes.
   d. When the rabbit was found under a pecan tree.
3. There is a moral to this story. Can you tell what it is?
4. Plan a story hour of folk tales. There are really four short tales in this story. Let members of your class tell these. Try to find other Mexican folk tales. Perhaps other pupils will prepare stories from Uncle Remus or other folk tales.

How Fire Comes From Sticks

A Legend

Many centuries ago, when the earth was young, there was a great drouth in the land of the Toltecs. The streams dried up, the fishes and animals died, and the Indians faced starvation. Seeing their plight, the great sun god, who they thought created man, fishes, and animals, caused it to rain, thus to provide food for his people.

But the god of evil slipped in one night and stole away their fire. Far away he traveled with it, almost to the land of the setting sun, where he gave it into the keeping of two old hags.

These two hags lived together in a little house on the top of a hill, where they could watch in every direction for outsiders. They never ceased their watching, not even to sleep. In their house the only flame in all the world burned day and night.

When the people no longer had fire, they could not cook their food, and they could not keep warm in winter. So great was their distress that they held a council to see what could be done. Someone suggested that the coyote be asked to help them recover the fire.

The coyote, who was the most cunning of all the animals, readily agreed to help the Indians in their trouble. He worked out a plan and called on many animals and people to help him. He stationed them all the way from the land of the Toltecs to the far distant place where the old hags lived. Only the strongest and the swiftest were asked to help. On the edge of the hill near where the hags dwelt he put one of the wisest and most trusted of the Indians. This done, he went boldly to the home of the hags and knocked on the door.

When one of the witches opened it, he told her that he was a weary traveler, and that he wanted to rest awhile from his travels. The two old women admitted him, and so graciously did he talk that they allowed him to remain for the night in their little house on top of the hill.

All night he lay on the floor of the hags' home pretending to sleep, but really he was watching for a chance to steal the fire. The old hags were so alert, though, that he soon saw that he could never gain possession of the precious fire without further planning. The next morning he excused himself and went out to have a talk with the Indian who was stationed nearest the house. They agreed that the Indian should attract the attention of the hags, at which time the coyote would run off with the fire.

The coyote went back to the house and lay down on the floor with his head on his paws, the way he had rested all night. Presently the Indian knocked so loudly on the door that it seemed as if he would break it down. Both of the old hags rushed out to see what was the matter.

This gave the coyote his chance. As the hags went out of the door, he seized the flaming brand in his teeth and leaped through a window. Away he galloped over the ground as fast as he could go.

The old hags saw him and gave chase. Because they had superhuman power, they gained rapidly on the coyote. Just as they reached out to seize him, he threw the brand to the fox, who then darted ahead on the second lap of the race. When the hags had almost caught the fox, he threw the fire to the antelope, and so on and on and on.

The last of all the animals to receive it was the frog. By this time it was only a spark. The frog took it in his mouth, swallowed it, and dived into the water. So close upon him were the hags that they almost caught him; in fact they did grab his tail and pulled it off trying to hold him. Since then, the frog has had no tail.

He swam and swam a long distance under the water; but as he neared the shore, he saw the old hags coming. He jumped into a pile of brush, spat out the fire, turned and jumped back into the water.

By that time the spark of fire was so small that the hags could not see it, but it remained in the brush where it has been ever since. Soon afterward the Indians learned that by rubbing together two dry sticks they could produce the precious fire. Ever afterward they had it for cooking and keeping warm.

— *J. A. Rickard*

Things to Do

1. A legend is a story that tells how or why certain things are believed to have happened. What were the Indians in the story trying to explain? Do you know the answer today?

2. This story would make an interesting play.
   a. How many scenes would you need?
   b. How many characters?
   c. What kind of props would be needed?
   d. Are sound effects necessary?
3. Invite another class to see your dramatization.
4. Someone might also tell your visitors how primitive people, like these Indians, tried to explain things that they did not understand.
5. Why was fire so important to the Indians?
6. Have some member of the class demonstrate the method the Indians used in making fire from sticks.

The First Americans

Indian Corn

Many people who read European books or the Bible know that the "corn" spoken of in them is wheat, and not the corn which is raised on farms in the United States. That grain, which is sometimes called Indian corn, is a native of the Americas. The Europeans knew nothing about it until they discovered America, nor did the Indians know anything about wheat.

This is well-known, but not many are aware that the ancestor of this Indian corn is a grass-like plant known as *teosinte.* It is very much like the Johnson grass which every farmer knows and dislikes. However, it is more canelike in the way it grows. It also produces a small ear of grain that resembles an ear of popcorn, except that it is much smaller.

This *teosinte,* as the Indians called it, was first grown on the rocky soil of Mexico, in a region called *tierra caliente* (hot country) not far from the Gulf of Mexico. Many centuries ago the Indians living in that region learned that when the *teosinte* plant was taken to a richer soil the ears of grain would grow larger. Other Indians learned to eat the grain and to grow it, until it was raised in almost every part of North and South America. By that time it had been improved until it was a large plant such as one sees in cornfields today.

The Aztec Indians parched the grains of this plant and ate them. They also soaked the grains in water and pounded or ground them to pieces between rough stones until they were made into meal which they mixed with water until it was a heavy dough. First rolling it out into thin layers they placed it on hot stones or in ovens over fires.

Corn cooked in this way made a thin cake called a *tortilla*. It was eaten with beans, or with ground meat mixed with pepper, tomatoes, or other foods, placed between the folds of the *tortilla*. The Indians did not have knives, forks, or spoons; the *tortilla* served for all of those utensils.

There is a story about the white man's first introduction to the *tortilla*. It was told that when the Spanish general, Cortés, invaded Mexico his servant was met by the servant of the Aztec ruler, Montezuma, whose capital then was where Mexico City now stands.

Naturally, the two servants wanted to impress each other with the greatness of their masters. The Spaniard began his bragging first.

"My king is king of the ocean, as well as of the land," he told the Aztec servant.

"But *my* king is king of two oceans and much land," replied the Aztec with a wave of his hands to the east and the west. This was true in a way, for the Aztec country extended from the Gulf of Mexico to the Pacific Ocean. Not to be outdone, the Spaniard spoke again.

"My king eats all his meals with silver spoons," he said.

"Oh, that is nothing," was the reply of the Aztec. "*My* king never eats out of the same spoon twice." That was also true, for the *tortilla* was Montezuma's spoon, and he ate it up!

It did not take the white men and women long to learn that corn was a good food; and they cooked it in many ways. One favorite way was to fill with corn meal dough an old fashioned vessel, with a lid to close it. This was placed on hot coals at the front of the big fireplace. Perhaps they put some lard or other fat in it, and when it was cooked brown it was delicious. Such a dish was known as a Johnny cake. People who traveled long distances found it easy to cook these cakes over outdoor fires, and for that reason they were sometimes called "journey cakes."

These cakes were not only good to eat, they were also healthful. It is said that modern machines which grind corn and wheat into meal and flour destroy some of the parts called vitamins which give strength. They now put back some of these vitamins, it is true, but the pioneers did not have to worry about vitamins — they only had to worry about how much to cook, for the whole family liked cornmeal pones and Johnny cakes so well that they ate many of them.

— *J. A. Rickard*

Things to Do

1. Compare the ways in which the Indians and pioneers used corn with the many uses of it today.
2. Use a World Almanac to find the corn production in this country since records have been kept.

Indian Signs

Indian children a long time ago did not go to school as children do now. They did not know how to write, but they did know how to express themselves by signs. Our boy and girl scouts today use some of the same signs that Indian children and their parents used long ago.

When an Indian set out on a journey, he seldom followed a road, for there were few. He placed stones in the ground to show his friends which way he had gone. If stones were not handy, and sometimes even if they were, he blazed a trail by cutting bark from trees that might be along his path. With his stone axe, or tomahawk, he could easily make a trail that friends could follow.

If the Indian lived on the prairie, where there were no trees, and if there were no stones, he had to use other signs. Since he almost always carried a blanket, he made signs with that. He would get on a high hill, where he could be seen for a long way, and wave his blanket. If he caught it by two corners and waved

it full size, his friends knew that meant danger. If he caught his blanket with both hands and ran back and forth with it, they knew he had found game. Perhaps he was telling them to hurry because ·he had seen a herd of buffaloes. If he held his blanket high on a pole, he was urging them please to hurry! hurry! hurry!

Indians also used smoke signals, which could be seen over long distances. Each tribe had different signals, so that friends could "read" them but enemies could not. The Indian had to build his signal fire carefully. First, he started a blazing fire, with a circle of dirt around it. Then he piled green or damp grass on it. This caused it to make much smoke but little fire, for anything green or damp will not burn easily.

With his fire making big smoke, the Indian, sometimes with the help of a companion, would stretch out a blanket above it, shutting off all smoke. Then, suddenly, they would remove the blanket, letting the smoke rise up into the air.

Each time the blanket was spread over the fire and removed, a small cloud of smoke went into the sky. Two of these smoke clouds might mean that an enemy was coming. Three of them might mean that buffaloes were near—and so on.

Indians were careful to guard against the spread of fires. They knew that fires could burn up grass and animals, and even homes. They put out fires with water before they left. If they had no water, they used green grass or dirt. They never left a fire burning. Perhaps that was another of their "signs." At least it was a sign that they knew danger when they saw it.

— J. A. Rickard

Things to Do

1. Make a list of the examples of sign language that are given in the story. Dramatize one of the signs and see if your classmates understand your message.
2. Discuss the kinds of sign language that we use today. Are traffic lights forms of sign language? Can you think of others?
3. How are sign language and reading alike?
4. How are our fire prevention rules like those of the Indians?

Sequoyah's Great Invention

Ah-yo-keh, the little Cherokee Indian girl, carried her cornhusk doll into the forest. She made a moss bed by the side of the brook for her doll, then flung herself on her stomach and trailed her hand in the clear, cool water. Ah-yo-keh was troubled. She was remembering what Pawlee, the corn-woman, had said to her mother only that morning.

Pawlee had set down the basket of corn which she left at the door every week. Then she had looked carefully around to be sure that no one could overhear.

The corn-woman had said to Ah-yo-keh's mother, "I warn you because I am your friend. Our people have begun to say that your husband is making magic against the tribe. All day long he makes marks on birch bark; and he mutters and makes strange sounds, as one who talks with evil powers."

Now, alone in the cool, green forest, Ah-yo-keh thought of the corn-woman's message. She remembered the last time she had been to the village with her father. Some braves had stared at him with unfriendly eyes.

Ah-yo-keh could not believe that her father

was a dealer in magic. Her father was kind and good. Why did the tribe think him a worker in evil?

Snatching up her doll, the little girl ran now to the spot where her father was working.

Sequoyah was sitting on a log not far from their cabin. From behind the bushes the child watched him quietly. Her heart leaped in doubt. Could the tribesmen be right? Her father sat with his head thrown back and his eyes closed. He was making queer sounds. Now and then he would take up a piece of birch bark and make a mark on it.

Ah-yo-keh stepped out from behind the bush and, with trembling voice, asked, "Father, what are you doing?"

Sequoyah put aside the bark and lit his pipe. He drew the child to the log beside him. "It is a long story. You must listen carefully," he said.

"Some years ago, when I was a young brave, I saw a white man looking at some paper on which there were many black marks. The white man told me these marks made a message on the paper. I thought how wonderful that the white men can send messages to people who are miles away. And I thought how wonderful it would be if the Cherokees could do the same.

"The white man, I told myself, is in many ways wiser than the Indian. The white nations are strong. Is this because of the written messages? On paper the white man can write down the wisdom each generation learns. Then later generations can learn that same wisdom."

Ah-yo-keh nodded, and her father went on. "I began to try to find a way to write our Cherokee language. The white man's marks cannot do for Cherokee words, because there are sounds in our language which cannot be made with the white man's marks.

"Then I began trying to find a mark for each of our sounds, to make what the white man calls an alphabet. That is why I sit here, trying to remember all the sounds in Cherokee talk. When I think of a sound, I make a mark for it. Now I am almost finished. Soon the Cherokee people will have an alphabet. Then they will be able to read and write."

Ah-yo-keh listened carefully while her father was speaking. But when he was finished she was still troubled. "But why do people think you are making magic against the tribe?"

"If I can finish my alphabet and make the tribe understand what I am doing, they will not have such foolish thoughts. They will thank me," answered her father.

"I will help you with the alphabet," the little girl said.

Sequoyah smiled, then told his daughter to go into the woods to gather more birch bark. He needed much of it, he said, for he made many mistakes.

But Ah-yo-keh said, "I will gather bark. But I also wish to help make marks."

Sequoyah's face brightened with gladness. "And why not!" He almost shouted in his excitement as a new thought came to him. "I will teach you to read and write. When the chiefs see that even a child can understand the marks, they will know there is no evil in them."

After that Ah-yo-keh spent many long hours with her father. Over and over she made the marks which represented sounds in the Cherokee language.

One day the brother of Sequoyah came to the cabin. He sat a long time smoking his pipe. Finally he spoke. "The chiefs are angry," he said. "They believe you make a magic to bring injury to the Cherokee nation."

Sequoyah answered his brother. "If the chiefs will come to my cabin, I shall prove to them that I do not perform magic against my tribe," he said. "I shall show them that what I do is for the good of my people."

The brother shook his head sadly and left the cabin.

Soon after that, the Cherokee chiefs announced that they would hold an investigation. And for this purpose they went in a body to Sequoyah's cabin. Their faces were solemn. They stood facing Sequoyah.

Ah-yo-keh took some pieces of birch bark to her father. Intently the chiefs examined them. Then one of them spoke. "If there is good in these pieces of birch bark, you must show us that good."

"I will prove to you that the writing is good," said Sequoyah. "My daughter will help me. I

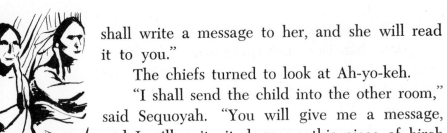

shall write a message to her, and she will read it to you."

The chiefs turned to look at Ah-yo-keh.

"I shall send the child into the other room," said Sequoyah. "You will give me a message, and I will write it down on this piece of birch bark. After that, take the bark to the child. She will read from it what your words have been."

Obediently, Ah-yo-keh went into the next room. "If only I am able to read the messages correctly," she thought.

When the chiefs took her the piece of birch bark on which were some familiar marks, the girl's hand shook so that she could scarcely hold it before her eyes. But her voice was clear and steady as she read the words, exactly as the chiefs had spoken them to her father in the next room.

The chiefs looked at one another in amazement. Could this thing be true? Perhaps the child had overheard what they said!

The chiefs returned to Ah-yo-keh's father and told him of their doubt.

"No," said Sequoyah. "My daughter did not overhear the message. She read it on the birch bark. But come! Since you do not believe that this is possible, let us go into the woods, far from the cabin. Once again we will send a message to my daughter."

The chiefs did as Sequoyah suggested. Far from the cabin they gave him a message. Again the message was taken to Ah-yo-keh, and again the child read it, exactly as it had been spoken.

The chiefs talked among themselves. At last the oldest of the chiefs said to Sequoyah, "This thing that you and your daughter have done is truly amazing. Is it possible that you can teach it to others?"

Sequoyah nodded. "If a child can master the marks," he answered, "surely our young men should not find the learning hard."

And so it was that Sequoyah became the teacher of his people. In just a few months' time, thousands of Cherokees learned to read and write. Then the tribe held a great feast in honor of the man who had invented their alphabet.

Ah-yo-keh was happy to think that her father had really helped their people. And Sequoyah himself was pleased, though his new honors did not make him vain. "Ability to write down sound is a gift of the Great Spirit," he said, "and the only reward I want is the privilege of teaching others."

For the rest of his life that is what he did. He was never too busy to stop work to explain his alphabet. Sometimes he traveled through the Cherokee settlements, teaching all who would learn.

And so it was that Sequoyah is remembered, not only by the Cherokee Indians but by all scholars, for he is the only man in the world who is known for making an alphabet by himself.

— *J. A. Rickard*
and Evelyn C. Nevin

Things to Do

1. This story could be made into a radio play or a dramatization. Who are the characters? Divide the

story into scenes. How many scenes are there? Would sound effects be needed?

2. Why did Sequoyah say that the white man's alphabet could not be used with Cherokee words?

3. Did you know that a tree is named for Sequoyah?

Statue of Sequoyah in the Capitol at Washington, D. C. Another such statue is in Calhoun, Georgia.

El Viajero [1] (The Traveler)

José Armijo[2] urges his team
As they crawl at the pace of a snail;
The mountains steep and the canyons deep
Can be seen from the rocky trail.
On either side is the forest wide:
Balsam, tall spruce, and pine;
The fragrant breeze stirs the tops of the trees,
And the air is like old wine.

José has come from his distant home
In the settlement far below;
He must not delay on his homeward way —
Ere long will come the snow.
He camped last night where the pale starlight
Sifts down on a mountain stream;
And, rolled in his blankets beside the fire,
Heard a mountain lion scream.

---

[1] vē ä hä′ rō   [2] är mē′ hō

His team is fed from the wagon bed,
While he gathers sticks for his fire;
He piles on wood, and the heat feels good
When the ruddy flames leap higher.
There's a chill in the air, though the skies are fair,
And a hint of winter's cold;
In the valley the leaves of the cottonwood
Are turning to brown and gold.

When the coals are red he bakes his bread
In the lee of the evergreens;
With coffee hot from the smoke-stained pot,
Tortillas, chili, and beans,
He prepares his meal; it's all he'll need
Till he reaches his journey's end;
For he knows that tonight, when stars are bright,
He'll sleep at the home of a friend.

— *Ethel M. Bolton*

Glossary

Glossary

Guide to Pronunciation

A.

ab-rupt'ly (ăb-rŭpt'lĭ). Suddenly, without warning

ab-sorbed' (ăb-sôrbd'). Buried in some thought or act

ac-com'mo-da'tions (ă-kŏm'ō-dā'shŭns). Food and lodging at a place

ac-com'plish (ă-kŏm'plĭsh). To complete or fulfill

al-cal'de (äl-käl'dā). A Spanish word for mayor of a town

a-lert' (à-lĕrt'). Wide-awake; brisk; nimble

al-le'giance (ă-lē'jăns). Devotion or loyalty to one's country

an-noy'ance (ă-noi'ăns). Trouble, a nuisance

ar-til'ler-y (är-tĭl'ēr-ĭ). Cannon; mounted guns

as'cer-tain (ăs'ēr-tān'). To find out or learn if a certain thing is true

as-sem'ble (ă-sĕm'b'l). To meet together

as-so'ci-ate (ă-sō'shĭ-āt). To join as a friend

at-tend'ant (ă-tĕn'-dănt). Guide, helper or servant

a-vail' (à-vāl'). To be of use; to serve a purpose

a-yun'ta-mien'to (ä-yōōn'tä-myän'tô). A Spanish word for city government

B.

ban'ter-ing (băn'tēr-ĭng). Teasing good-naturedly

bev'-er-age (bĕv'ēr-ĭj). Liquid for drinking

birch (bûrch). A tree having a hard, close-grained wood

bolt'ing (bōlt'ĭng). Starting swiftly like an arrow or dart

burnt of'fer-ing (bûrnt ŏf'ēr-ĭng). A gift that is burned as an offering to a god

C.

camp meet'ing (kămp' mēt'-ĭng). Religious gathering

cam-paign' (kăm-pān'). A military operation

can'tle (kăn't'l). The upward-curving rear part of a saddle

cir'cum-stance (sûr'kŭm-stăns). An event or happening in a course of affairs

clev'is (klĕv'ĭs). A piece of metal used on the end of the tongue of a wagon

col'o-niz-ing (kŏl'ô-nīz-ĭng). Making or starting colonies

com-mis'sion (kŏ-mĭsh'ŭn). A written statement granting power and authority to perform certain duties

309

Glossary

com-po'sure (kŏm-pō'zhẽr). Being settled or calm

con-sume' (kŏn-sūm'). To destroy as by fire

con-tin'gent (kŏn-tĭn'jĕnt). A number of persons or troops

con-tin'u-ous (kŏn-tĭn'ŭ-ŭs). Without stopping

coun'te-nance (koun'tḗ-nǎns). The expression of the face of a person

D.

de-ceive' (dḗ-sēv'). To cheat or mislead

de-ci'sion (dḗ-sĭzh'ŭn). Deciding or settling a matter

de-lir'i-ous (dḗ-lĭr'ĭ-ŭs). Raving or "out of one's head"

dep'u-ty mar'shal (dĕp'ŭ-tĭ mär'shǎl). One who is appointed to act for the marshal whose duties are like those of a sheriff

de-scend' (dḗ-scend'). To go down to a place

dis-patch' (dĭs-pǎtch'). To send off quickly; to end business speedily

de-vour'ing (dḗ-vour'ĭng) Eating greedily

dex'ter-ous (dĕk'stẽr-ŭs). Skillful or expert

din (dĭn). A loud noise or deafening uproar

dis-as'trous (dĭ-zás'trŭs). Full of misfortune causing great loss

dis-mount' (dĭs-mount'). To get down from a horse or a bicycle

dis-tress' (dĭs-trĕs'). Danger; grief

drift fence (drĭft fĕns). A long straight fence running east and west

E.

em'i-grant (ĕm'ĭ-grǎnt). One who goes from a country to settle elsewhere

em'i-gra'tion (ĕm'ĭ-grā'shŭn). Departure from a country for life elsewhere

en-dure' (ĕn-dūr'). To bear pain or misfortune with patience

en-rage' (ĕn-rāj'). To fill with anger

en'ter-prise (ĕn'tẽr-prīz). An undertaking that is daring or important

es'cort (ĕs'kôrt). One who goes with another for protection

ex-pir'ing (ĕk-spīr'ĭng). Ending, dying, ceasing

F.

for-ma'tion (fôr-mā'shŭn). An arrangement or order, as in a line

fran'ti-cal-ly (frăn'tĭ-câl-ĭ). Wildly; in frenzied manner

fre-quent' (frḗ-kwĕnt'). To visit often

fre'quent-ly (frḗ'kwĕnt-lĭ). At frequent or short intervals; often

G.

gen'er-a'tion (jĕn'ẽr-ā'shŭn). Descent; offspring

310

Glossary

girth (gûrth). A band around the body of a horse, to fasten a saddle

grooms'man (grōomz'măn). A male friend who attends a bridegroom at his wedding

H.

haz'ard (hăz'ĕrd). Risk; danger

heart'i-ly (här'tĭ-lĭ). With zest and fun

hos'pi-ta-ble (hŏs'pĭ-tȧ-b'l). Receiving and entertaining strangers kindly

host (hōst). One who entertains or receives another

hos'tage (hŏs'tĭj). A person who is kept for the fulfillment of a pledge or treaty

hos'tile (hŏs'tĭl). Having or showing ill will; unfriendly

I.

in'di-ca'tions (ĭn'dĭ-kā'shŭns). Signs

in'di-rect'ly (ĭn'dĭ-rĕkt'lĭ). In a roundabout way

in'di-vis'i-ble (ĭn'dĭ-vĭz'ĭ-b'l). Cannot be divided into parts

in-fu'ri-ate (ĭn-fū'rĭ-āt). To make very angry

in-im'i-ta-ble (ĭn-ĭm'ĭ-tȧ-b'l). Cannot be matched

in-i'ti-ate (ĭ-nĭsh'ĭ-āt). To admit into a club by a special ceremony

in'-of-fen'sive (ĭn'ŏ-fĕn'sĭv). Harmless

in'tu-i'tion (ĭn'tŭ-ĭsh'ŭn). The power of knowing without thought or study

in-vade (ĭn-vād'). To enter for conquest or plunder

in-ves'ti-ga'tion (ĭn-vĕs'tĭ-gā'shŭn). Careful examination

J.

jour-ney-cake' (jûr'nĭ-kāk). In America called "johnny-cake," a bread made of Indian meal, flour, eggs, milk, etc.

K.

L.

lack'ing (lăk'ing). Wanting or missing

lease (lēs). A contract for a number of years, which allows a person to use or hold property

le'gal-ize (lē'găl-īz). To make legal or according to law

lit'er-al-ly (lĭt'ĕr-ăl-ĭ). True to fact; not exaggerated

M.

mal'lard (măl'ĕrd). A common wild duck

mar'tyr (mär'tĕr). One who gives his life for something he believes

mas'sa-cre (măs'ȧ-kĕr). The cruel killing of human beings

mill'ing (mĭl'ĭng). Moving in a small circle or in an uncertain way

more-o'ver (mōr-ō'vĕr). Further; beyond what has been said

mu'ti-lat-ed (mū'tĭ-lāt-ĕd). Broken, cut or maimed

Glossary

N.

no'ta-ble (nō'tȧ-b'l). Remarkable; distinguished

O.

op'po-si'tion (ŏp'ȯ-zĭsh'ŭn). Resistance, striving against by argument

or'der-ly (ôr'dēr-lĭ). A soldier who attends a superior officer to carry out his orders

out-wit' (out-wĭt'). To succeed by greater wisdom or cunning.

P.

pa'tri-ot (pā'trĭ-ŭt). One who loves his country

pe-ti'tion (pė-tĭsh'ŭn). A written request

pin'to (pĭn'tō). Spanish word that means painted or mottled

pla'za (plä'zȧ). Spanish word for a public square in the center of a town

plight (plīt). A condition or state

plun'der (plŭn'dēr). To take by force; to commit robbery or to steal

pone (pōn). Corn bread made without eggs or milk

pow'der box (pou'dēr bŏx). A thing or situation that could explode or burn easily

pre-sid'ed (prė-zīd'ĕd). Directed or had charge of

pre'vi-ous-ly (prē'vĭ-ŭs-lў). Earlier or before

prey (prā). Any animal seized by another to be eaten

prong'horn' (prŏng'hôrn'). A peculiar antelope of the treeless parts of the Western United States and Mexico

pro-por'tion-ate-ly (prȯ-pōr'-shŭn-ĭt-lў). In right proportions or shares

pro-pos'al (prȯ-pōz'ăl). An offer or plan

prop'o-si'tion (prŏp'ȯ-zĭsh'ŭn). An offer or proposal

pros'e-cu'tion (prŏs'ė-kū'-shŭn). Carrying out plans; starting a suit in a court of law.

pro-vi'sions (prȯ-vĭzh'ŭns). Food and other supplies

pru'dent (prōō'dĕnt). Behaving wisely or cautiously

pun'cheons (pŭn'chŭns). Pieces of heavy split timber

pur-sue' (pēr-sū). To follow

pur-su'ing (pēr-sū'ĭng). Chasing or following

Q.

R.

ra-vine' (rȧ-vēn'). A large gully

read'i-ly (rĕd'ĭ-lĭ). With promptness; quickly

re-bel'ling (rė-bĕl'lĭng). Opposing one in authority

re-cruit' (rė-krōōt). A newly enlisted soldier

re-sist'ance (rė-zĭs'tăns). An opposing force

re-straints' (rė-straints'). Controls over one's thoughts, feelings or actions

Glossary

re-treat′ (rê-trēt′). The withdrawal from the presence of an enemy

re-veal′ing (rê-vēl′ĭng). Showing something that is secret or hidden

re-verse (rê-vûrs). Misfortune, defeat

roup (rōōp). A disease of poultry

rout (rōut). To defeat completely

Roy′al-ist (Roi′ăl-ĭst). A person who was loyal to the Spanish king

S.

sad′dle-bags′ (săd′l-băgs′). A large double bag or pouch carried hanging across a saddle

sap′ling (săp′lĭng). A young tree

scur′ry (skûr′ĭ). To scamper or hurry

sec′tion (sĕk′shŭn). 640 acres of land

sem′i-cir′cle (sĕm′ĭ-sûr′k′l). Half of a circle

sen′si-tive (sĕn′sĭ-tĭv). Capable of being easily excited or stimulated

so-journ′ (sô-jûrn′). To stay for a short time

sor′rel (sŏr′ĕl). A reddish-brown horse

squat′ted (skwŏt′ĕd). To settle on new or unoccupied land

sta′tion-ed (stā′shŭn′d). Put at a certain place

sŭm′mon (sŭm′ŭn). To call

sus-pi′cion (sŭs-pĭsh′ŭn). To think, without proof, that something is not all right

T.

tal′ly (tăl′ĭ). To keep a score by notches or marks

ten′der-foot′ (tĕn′dẽr-fŏŏt′). A newcomer in a newly settled country

te-o-sin′te (tā-ō-sĭn′tā). Indian corn

tor-tí-lla (tŏr-tē′yä). A Mexican word for thin, unleavened bread

trai′tor (trā′tẽr). One who betrays a confidence or trust

U.

ud′der (ŭd′ẽr). A milk gland with four teats or nipples, as in cows

un-err′ing (ŭn-ûr′ĭng). Certain; unfailing.

V.

vain (vān). Foolish or silly; having too high an opinion of oneself

vault′ed (vôlt′ĕd). Jumped or climbed astride a horse

vi-cin′i-ty (vĭ-sĭn′ĭ-tĭ). Nearby, close

vic′tor (vĭk′tẽr). A winner in a contest or struggle

W.

weap′on (wĕp′ŭn). Something to fight with

wind′fall′ (wĭnd′fŏl′). Unexpected good fortune

wir′y (wīr′ĭ). Like wire

wist′ful-ly (wĭst′fŏŏl-ĭ). Wanting something very much and not expecting to get it

To the Teacher

To the Teacher:

As you know, reading abilities and interests of children in the intermediate grades cover a wide range, this range often extending from the fourth to the tenth grade.

It is true, also, that reading *materials* for children in the intermediate grades show a great range and variety.

A prominent educator has recently pointed out that the areas in which demands for increased reading skill in intermediate grades will be made, are:

First: Children should continue to enjoy recreational material, but their reading should include many different types of fiction, poetry, biography, and informational material. As they read more widely, they should become more discriminating in their tastes. They can be expected to develop standards for evaluating what they read, to become interested in special authors and illustrators, and to enjoy different writing styles.

Second: There should be much wider use of informational materials. In the intermediate grades these include textbooks to a much greater extent than they did earlier. In many schools children will work with five or six books in a given subject-matter area rather than with a single adopted text. Standard encyclopedias, atlases, almanacs, and other compilations should be used more frequently. The more mature children should also be able to follow much of the news in the daily paper, to locate articles in current magazines, and to read pamphlets. Of all the new demands made on older children, those occasioned by this greatly increased variety of informational materials are likely to be among the heaviest.

To the Teacher

Third: Intermediate-grade children should show increased skill in evaluating what they read in terms of their purposes. In recreational reading this should result in wider acquaintance with authors and illustrators, in increased sensitivity to differences in writing style, and in increased insight in selecting books for varied purposes. In informational reading intermediate-grade children should be able to make more discriminating decisions regarding the appropriateness of material to their problems. Perhaps more important, they should be able to handle more complex problems of appraising the accuracy of what they read—deciding how to check when textbooks disagree; determining a writer's qualifications; distinguishing between editorial writing and news reporting; distinguishing fact from fiction.[1]

The stories in this book may be used to enrich the reading experiences of your class in the following ways:

(1) As supplementary reading for the entire class or for small groups.

(2) As a source of information for small groups within the class who are working upon problems in social studies.

(3) For the personal reading of children who are interested in the history of the Southwest.

The stories in this book are intended, also, to enrich and expand the content usually found in textbooks in social studies and in basal readers. A few selections, written by persons who lived at or near the time the events occurred, were taken di-

---

[1]Margaret McKim, *Guiding Growth in Reading* (New York: The Macmillan Co., 1955), p. 318.

To the Teacher

rectly from their original sources. The language used is that of the authors except in rare cases where necessary to simplify for children. The folk tales were included to help children understand the primitive peoples of the Southwest. Other stories are "historical fiction;" that is, they were placed in their true historical settings with fictional plots and characters.

The poems have been selected because they give added appreciation for the stories in the sections in which they are placed. They may be shared with the entire class through oral reading. Some of these poems may be adapted for choral reading and enjoyed by the total group.

The *Things to Do* at the end of each story are suggestions for activities that may help children meet some of the demands of reading in intermediate grades. They may be used in presenting the stories, or they may be used as aids to the interpretation of the selections.

Two specific things were kept in mind as the activities were planned:

(1) The problems suggested require the use of reading skills that the children need: evaluating what is read; organizing and summarizing materials; and interpreting graphs, maps, and charts.

(2) Provision was made for children to use the materials in creative ways. Reading about a subject is not enough to make learning effective; materials from stories have to be used in creative ways to become the child's own. Therefore, dramatization, making of movies, TV shows, maps, and illustrations were suggested often.

To the Teacher

In selecting for the glossary the words and meanings unique to the stories, and in order to avoid the use of words too difficult for the respective grade levels, well-known vocabulary studies were consulted. Because of the great differences in the abilities of children to attack words and the wide range in reading vocabularies, it was difficult to select the words for the glossary. Only the uncommon and seemingly more difficult words are presented. No attempt was made to meet the vocabulary needs of all children. Individual children should be encouraged to use dictionaries for words not included in the glossary.

It is the hope of the authors that, besides contributing to greater reading achievement, this book will give to children who use it a deeper understanding of our country's present through its attempt to make the past come alive. Also, it is their hope that children may find increased insight into their own problems by an understanding of the people in earlier times and places.

Acknowledgments

The authors and publishers wish to express their grateful thanks to all who have assisted in the preparation of the material in this book — for their constructive criticism, for assistance in reading proof, and for otherwise helping in editorial and artwork.

Also, to the following organizations and persons who have graciously permitted the use of material, they gratefully acknowledge their obligation: to JACK & JILL for *Narciso — A Mexican Boy Hero, Temo and the Emperor, The Banner — Bird and Bush,* and *Sequoyah;* to JUNIOR LIFE for *Donkey for Rent, The Shoe Gobbler,* and *Big Horns and the New Fence;* to CHILDREN'S ACTIVITIES for *Alone on the Range, Frank and His Friend Mallie, Indian Corn,* and *Indian Signs;* to Mrs. William Dyer Moore for *Weaving Time in Texas;* to DAVID McKAY COMPANY for *Call Up Adventure and Let Us Ride, The Plowman* and *The Settlers;* to THE MACMILLAN COMPANY for material from *Guiding Growth in Reading* by Margaret McKim; and to the NEW MEXICO MAGAZINE for *El Viajero,* by Ethel M. Bolton.